This book i⬛
you are an⬛

bodybuilder
fitness trainee
strength trainee
powerlifter

The emphasis you place on weight training will vary according to your specific interest, and the degree of size and strength you desire. But the pool of exercises you can select from is universal to almost everyone who lifts weights.

When you lift weights, the bottom line is the same no matter who you are, what your goals are, or where you train:

> *If you want your training to be successful, and not cause injuries, you must use correct exercise technique.*

Without correct exercise technique, your physique, strength or fitness goals will never be achieved.

But the use of correct exercise technique is the exception in nearly all gyms, not the rule. Don't expect to learn it from a gym.

Step-by-step, this book will teach you how to use correct exercise technique.

ALSO BY STUART MCROBERT

Brawn

Beyond Brawn

Further Brawn

Build Muscle, Lose Fat, Look Great

The Muscle and Might Training Tracker

The Insider's Tell-All Handbook On
Weight-Training Technique
3RD EDITION

363 PHOTOS

THE ILLUSTRATED STEP-BY-STEP GUIDE TO PERFECTING YOUR EXERCISE FORM FOR INJURY-FREE MAXIMUM GAINS

Stuart McRobert

CS Publishing Ltd., P.O. Box 20390, CY-2151 Nicosia, Cyprus
tel + 357-2233-3069   cspubltd@spidernet.com.cy
www.hardgainer.com

US office: CS Publishing Ltd., P.O. Box 1002, Connell, WA 99326
tel 509-234-0362   info@hardgainer.com
www.hardgainer.com

Printed in the United States of America

Cataloging-in-Publication Data

McRobert, Stuart
   The insider's tell-all handbook on
weight-training technique / Stuart McRobert. --
3rd ed.
   p. cm.

   ISBN: 978-9963-9163-2-0

   1. Weight training--Handbooks, manuals, etc.   I. Title
GV546.M37 2009
   796.41

Table of contents

Introduction   *10*

PART 1

How to train safely   *14*
Rep speed and control   *28*
The four main hand grips   *30*
A primer on anatomy   *32*

PART 2
How to master exercise technique   *46*

1. Back extension	*basic back extension*	*54*
	45-degree back extension	*57*
	spinal extension	*57*
	machine back extension	*58*
2. Bench press	*barbell bench press*	*60*
	dumbbell bench press	*68*
	close-grip bench press	*72*
	incline barbell bench press	*76*
	incline dumbbell bench press	*80*
3. Calf raise	*standing two-legged calf raise*	*84*
	standing one-legged calf raise	*86*
4. Chin-up (and pull-up)		*88*
5. Crunch	*basic crunch*	*94*
	modified basic crunch	*96*
	machine crunch	*97*
	reverse crunch	*98*
	twisting crunch	*100*
6. Curl	*seated dumbbell curl*	*104*
	incline dumbbell curl	*105*
	barbell curl	*106*
	hammer curl	*107*
7. Deadlift	*deadlift (basic, or conventional deadlift)*	*112*
	parallel-grip deadlift	*122*
	partial deadlift	*130*
	sumo deadlift	*134*
8. Finger extension		*136*
9. Hand-gripper work	*torsion-spring gripper*	*139*
	Ivanko super gripper	*141*
10. Lateral raise	*dumbbell lateral raise*	*144*
	machine lateral raise	*145*
11. Leg curl		*146*

12. Leg press		*150*
13. L-fly		*156*
14. Neck work	*manual resistance neck work*	*161*
	four-way neck machine	*162*
15. Parallel bar dip		*164*
16. Press	*seated barbell press*	*168*
	seated dumbbell press	*172*
17. Pulldown		*176*
18. Pullover	*machine pullover*	*180*
	breathing pullover	*184*
19. Pushdown		*186*
20. Rotary torso		*188*
21. Row	*one-arm dumbbell row*	*190*
	cable row	*192*
	seated machine row	*196*
	prone low-incline dumbbell row	*197*
22. Shrug		*198*
23. Side bend	*dumbbell side bend*	*203*
	pulley side bend	*205*
24. Squat	*squat (conventional or back squat)*	*212*
	front squat	*230*
	ball squat	*240*
	hip-belt squat	*244*
25. Timed hold		*250*

Supplementary exercises

26. Grip machine training	*254*
27. Lever bar work	*256*
28. Overhead lockout	*258*
29. Pinch-grip lifting	*262*
30. Rader chest pull	*266*
31. Wrist roller training	*268*

PART 3

How to handle weights between exercises	*274*
How to compose exercise technique checklists	*280*
Video recordings: the acid test of correct exercise technique	*282*
How to become flexible	*288*
About the author	*308*

Photography credits

I would like to thank the models, all of whom generously gave their time, and the gym owners, all of whom generously gave access to their premises. They were all wonderfully cooperative and patient.

Left, Ian Duckett, owner of Body in Design Gym, in Leeds, England. Above, from the left, Claire Cotter, Helen Everson, Jenny Garside, and Robin Gorry. All photographs of these trainees were taken at Ian's gym.

Left, Con Demetriou. All photographs of Con were taken by Mike Christofides at what was then Gold's Gym in Nicosia, Cyprus.

Left, Eleni Papadopoulos. All photographs of Eleni were taken at Olympus Gym in Nicosia, Cyprus.

Here are the credits for the other models appearing in this book:

Brian Breech, pages 118 (top right), 119 (left) and 135 (top left, and bottom left); Brian Carlton, pages 245 and 247; Chip Kent, pages 124, 132 and 133; Brian Rayner, page 118 (top left, and top middle); Derek Wallace, page 224; Bill Windscheif, pages 113 and 118 (bottom).

Introduction

Successful bodybuilding and any other type of weight training are among the most satisfying activities. Transforming your body is thrilling. But done improperly, training will damage your body. Training-related injuries are universal.

The same basic pool of exercises applies whether you're a bodybuilder, fitness enthusiast, strength trainee, or powerlifter. But to benefit from training you must be able to work out consistently and progressively. You can't do this if you repeatedly suffer from injuries. Abuse yourself with incorrect exercise technique for long enough and you'll be frustrated with one injury after another, and eventually do so much damage that you'll put an end to your days of hard training.

But don't be discouraged. Take comfort from knowing that, properly done, weight training is safe and super effective.

Correct exercise technique is needed not just to avoid training injuries. It's one of the requirements for stimulating the fastest rate of muscular development and strength gains.

This book will teach you the conservative forms of the most productive exercises. Without a conservative approach you'll be racked with so many injuries that you'll be unable to train consistently enough to achieve your goals. A few people have unusually tough bodies and are able to get away with incorrect exercise technique. But for each trainee who does get away with incorrect technique there are hundreds who don't.

Some people's advice for how to deal with exercises that are irritating is to drop poundage and do much higher reps. While increasing rep count and reducing poundage is sometimes desirable, it's usually a mere salve because the root of the problem—incorrect exercise technique—has not been corrected. If flawed technique is used, once the poundages are built up and the training becomes intensive, the problem that drove you to using high reps will resurface.

The education needed to write this book came from several sources. My own training experiences over many years make up only a part of the education. The publishing and editing of HARDGAINER magazine for 15 years gave me a deep insight into training. The education was bolstered by feedback from readers of my books, a lot of writing for newsstand bodybuilding magazines, answering countless questions, providing many hours of hands-on coaching, and extensive studying of training in general.

This book can save you years if not decades of wasted training. You can learn a wealth of useful information from just a few days of serious study. You no longer have to learn the hard way what constitutes correct exercise technique and its central importance in your training.

Don't assume that, because you've been performing an exercise for a long time, you know its proper technique. Please study all of this book no matter how experienced you are.

Please don't treat this book as a one-time read. There's far more information in it than can be absorbed from a single reading. Repeatedly refer to the book.

This book is your constant reference on exercise technique. But it doesn't cover program design. That's covered in my other books.

To your success,

Stuart McRobert

When I wrote BUILD MUSCLE, LOSE FAT, LOOK GREAT, I wanted to produce a complete book on exercise and physique transformation, so it had to include exercise technique. I took most of the text from the second edition of THE INSIDER'S TELL-ALL HANDBOOK ON WEIGHT-TRAINING TECHNIQUE, revised it and added many exercises, and produced Chapter 12 of BUILD MUSCLE. Then I took INSIDER'S out of print.

But then, in response to demand once again for a book on exercise technique alone, I took Chapter 12 from BUILD MUSCLE, LOSE FAT, LOOK GREAT, added some supplementary exercises and other additional material, and produced what you have here—the third edition of INSIDER'S.

But BUILD MUSCLE, LOSE FAT, LOOK GREAT includes about 400 pages on topics *other than* exercise technique.

PART 1

How to train safely   14
Rep speed and control   28
The four main hand grips   30
A primer on anatomy   32

I promote a conservative approach to training. Experience from more than thirty years—from my own personal training, and from observing countless other trainees—has taught me that the conservative approach isn't just the safest way, *it's also the most effective way over the long term*.

How to train safely

To progress in strength and physique, you must train regularly, but you can't do that if you experience injuries. Barring freak accidents, training injuries have nothing to do with bad luck. They have everything to do with ignorance, following bad advice, and inattentiveness. Done properly, strength training *is* safe.

The building of strength itself, provided it's done safely, helps protect against injury. Most injuries are a result of an imposed force exceeding the structural strength of the involved bodypart. If structural strength is increased, resistance to injury will be increased, too.

To help you to avoid injuries, here are 38 recommendations:

1. Never apply the "No pain, no gain" maxim

Never do anything that hurts, don't train if you've hurt yourself, and never train through pain. Cumulative muscular discomfort, and systemic fatigue from an exercise done with effort and correct technique, are desirable, but pain isn't. Any sharp, stabbing, or sudden pain is a sign you've injured yourself.

Countless trainees have given up strength training because of having been hurt from following foolish advice. Those who live the "No pain, no gain" maxim usually regret it, sooner or later.

2. Know your physical anomalies

Modify your training according to any physical anomalies you may have. For example, if you've had back surgery, the barbell squat may be an unwise exercise selection; and if you have foot problems, running wouldn't be a wise choice of cardio exercise. Know your body before you go training it.

3. Seek correction of physical restrictions

With the right treatment you may be able to rid yourself of problems you may have accepted as permanent, or at least reduce them greatly. Investigate the possibility. You probably have restrictions in your muscles—soft-tissue restrictions are at the root of many physical problems and limitations. Seek expert therapists. You may need to look beyond your home area.

4. Don't neglect flexibility work

Generally, supple muscles are less likely to suffer injury than tight ones. Supple muscles have more give in them than tight muscles, and help protect against injury. Supple *and* strong muscles provide greater protection.

5. Adapt to exercises

Be patient when learning how to perform a new exercise. Use very light weights to begin with, and only once you've mastered exercise technique should you add weight, gradually, and pick up the effort level.

Once you've had a lot of experience with a particular exercise but haven't included it in your program for a few months, take a few weeks to refamiliarize yourself with it before you train it hard.

6. Apply training discipline

It's easier to use correct technique and controlled rep speed at the start of a set than during the final few reps when the required effort is higher. Hold correct technique and controlled rep speed even on the final "can just squeeze this out" rep. Never break correct technique to force out another rep. Perform correct reps only, or end the set.

If possible, train with a partner who can scrutinize your technique and rep speed, and, by oral cues, help you to keep your technique and rep speed correct.

7. Use a safe range of motion

Use the maximum safe range of motion for you for each exercise. For selectorized equipment, such as many leg curl machines, you can manually delimit the range of motion, if required. Remove the pin from the weight stack, then grip the cable that's attached to the guide rod that runs through the weight stack, and lift it. The top weight plate will rise alone, revealing the guide rod. Expose two holes on the rod, for example, and then use the pin to select the required weight. The gap between the first and second weight plates indicates the reduction in range of motion—two to three inches in this illustration. Fine-tune the reduction to what's required to produce the maximum safe range of motion for you. Make a note in your training logbook of the setting.

8. Maintain symmetrical lifting

Other than for one-side-at-a-time exercises such as the one-legged calf raise, and the L-fly, focus on symmetrical technique, to apply symmetrical stress to your body.

Don't let the bar slope to one side during barbell work. Keep it parallel with the floor at all times. Both hands must move in unison. For example, in barbell pressing, one hand should neither be above nor in front of the other.

A critical factor behind symmetrical lifting, is symmetrical hand and foot positioning. If one hand is placed further from the center of the bar than the other, or if one foot is positioned differently to the other, you won't be symmetrically positioned, and thus will be set up for asymmetrical lifting.

Load barbells carefully. If you loaded one end of the bar with more weight than the other, you'll lift asymmetrically. A substantial weight difference will be noticeable during the first rep of a set, whereupon the bar should be set down or racked, and the loading corrected. A bar that's slightly lopsided may not be detectable, but will nevertheless lead to asymmetrical lifting, and perhaps injury.

If you lift on a surface that's not horizontal, you'll lift asymmetrically. Train on a level floor. This is especially important for the big exercises, such as the squat, deadlift, overhead press, and bench press. Take a spirit level to the gym, and check out whether or not the lifting areas are level, and then use only the ones that are.

9. Use proper head and eye control

Key factors in maintaining symmetrical lifting are a fixed, face-forward, *neutral* head position, and keeping your eyes riveted on one spot during a set. (A neutral head position is neither extended nor flexed.) Except for neck exercises, avoid any lateral, forward, or rearward movement of your head when you train with weights.

10. Keep your eyes open

If you close your eyes while training, you'll risk some deterioration of balance. There may also be degradation of bar control, especially in exercises that use free-weights. Both can threaten your safety. Don't close your eyes while you train.

11. Use the right weight selection for you

Use weights you can handle in correct technique. Most trainees use more weight than they can handle correctly. This leads to cheating, and a loss of control.

12. Choose safe exercises

An exercise that's safe for some trainees may not be for others. Because of physical anomalies, accidents, or other injuries, specific exercises may be proscribed.

Don't use exercises that aren't suited to you. If an exercise irritates a joint or causes sharp, stabbing, or sudden pain, don't persist with it. Fix the problem before returning to that exercise, or avoid the exercise if the cause of the problem can't be corrected.

13. Avoid high-risk lifting

All types of lifting weights can be dangerous if not done correctly, but some forms carry a higher risk than others. For example, rock lifting and other forms of handling awkwardly shaped objects carry a far higher risk of injury than barbell, dumbbell, and machine training.

14. Don't follow the examples of the genetic elite

A few trainees are so robust they can withstand training abuse that would cripple most trainees. But eventually even those robust trainees usually pay a heavy price.

Don't take liberties in the gym. For each trainee who can apparently get away with training liberties, there are many who pay a high price for such abuse.

15. When using machines, follow the manufacturers' instructions

For some exercises, you may have to line up a specific joint with the pivot point of the machine. The right set-up position is critical. Changing the seat's position (and thus your position) by just one peg, for example, can make a difference in the comfort of a given machine exercise.

To line up with accuracy a given point on a machine with a given point on your body, your eyes need to be at the same level as the points being lined up. This usually isn't practical, so get an assistant to line you up.

Once you have the right set-up for a specific exercise, make a written note in your training logbook of the seat or other setting you require, for reference.

If you've used a machine as the manufacturer advises (often through instructions fixed to the equipment), have tweaked the set-up to suit you, and have used smooth rep speed, and yet the exercise still irritates a joint, substitute an alternative exercise.

16. Don't squeeze machine handles more than necessary

On some machine exercises, such as the leg curl and the leg press, you need to stabilize yourself through holding onto handles or other grip supports. Don't squeeze the handles more than necessary to stabilize yourself. Intensive squeezing increases blood pressure.

17. Be safety conscious with equipment

Never begin an exercise without having first checked safety considerations. Check that bolts are tight, cables aren't frayed, cable connections are secure, rack pins are securely in position, adjustable weight saddles are fixed in place, locking pin(s) for adjustable benches and seats are secure, and benches are stable and strong. Never use dumbbells without checking that the collars are securely fixed. A dumbbell coming apart while in use, especially overhead, could be calamitous.

Just one accident could stop you training for a long time. Be careful.

Put collars on a loaded barbell securely. Plates on one end of the bar that slide out of position can disturb your balance and symmetry. Get a pair of light-weight, quick-release collars, if where you train doesn't have them. Allow a few millimeters, or a small fraction of an inch, between a collar and the outermost plate, to permit the plates to play.

18. Avoid singles and low reps

Any exercise performed in any rep range will hurt you if you use poor technique. If you always use correct technique, all rep counts can be comparatively safe, at least in theory. Your body must, however, be accustomed to the rep count you're using before you start to push yourself hard. This especially applies to singles (one-rep sets), and low-rep work (sets of two to four reps).

Comparing the same degree of technique error, if you get out of the ideal groove during a maximum single, you're more likely to hurt yourself than if you get out of the groove during a set of medium or high reps. But this doesn't mean that high reps with reduced weights are guaranteed to be safe. Even with high reps and reduced weights, if you use poor technique, you would be asking for injury.

Beginners should avoid singles, and low-rep work. Stick with medium or higher reps.

19. Don't train when you're muscularly very sore

Sore and tight muscles are easily injured. A little local soreness, however, especially for beginners, shouldn't prohibit training. When you're training once again following severe soreness, reduce your effort level a little, and build it back over several workouts, to prevent a repeat of the excessive soreness.

When you're sore, you may be more prone to injury. Give yourself extra rest before you train the sore area hard again. To help speed the easing of soreness, do some additional low-intensity aerobic work. Massage may also help, as may a hot bath. Paradoxically, another bout of the exercises that made you very sore—but very light and easy this time—may help relieve the soreness.

Being sore doesn't necessarily indicate that you've stimulated growth. Good soreness comes from hard work on exercises done correctly, is purely muscular, and goes away after a few days. This is different from longer-lasting soreness because of abusive exercise technique, or having trained too heavily, too much, or too hard too soon.

Some muscle groups show soreness more readily than others. That your shoulders, for example, may never get sore, doesn't mean they aren't getting trained. And that another muscle may get sore easily, doesn't necessarily mean that it's going to grow faster than a muscle that's rarely if ever sore.

20. Don't train when you're fatigued from a previous workout

If you're systemically wiped out—which may or may not be accompanied by muscular soreness—rest for an extra day or two, until you're raring to go again. Then when you're back in the gym, reduce your training volume or intensity, and build it back over several workouts, to permit your body to adapt. If you get wiped out again, and provided the components of recuperation are in order, there's something amiss with your training program, and you need to modify it—abbreviate it.

21. Take heed of a sore back

If you regularly experience a sore back during or after training, investigate the cause, and rectify it. A sore back is a warning that a back injury may be nigh unless corrective action is taken. A back injury is among the most debilitating of injuries.

22. Increase resistance in small increments

Small increases in exercise weights permit gradual, progressive resistance, in manageable doses. This is easy to do with free-weights provided you have fractional plates. These small plates weigh less than the 1.25 kilos or 2.5 pounds that are commonly the smallest plates in most gyms. Fractional plates are typically quarter, half, and one-pound discs (and 100, 250, and 500 grams).

Progressing from, say, 100 pounds to 110 in one jump, when 100 pounds was the most you could handle for 8 reps, is excessive. The 110 pounds—a 10% increase in resistance—would cause a substantial drop in reps and, in many cases, lead to a deterioration of exercise technique.

Even an increase to 105 pounds may be excessive. An increase to 101 pounds may, however, be barely perceptible. Then the next week you may be able to increase to 102 pounds, and so on.

With weight-stack machines, incremental progressive resistance can be difficult to achieve, because the weight jumps between stacks are usually excessive—typically 10 to 15 pounds per unit on the stack. The solution is to attach small increments to the weight stack, provided the design of the weight stack permits it. Push the weight selector pin through a small weight plate and *then* into the weight stack. Alternatively, attach magnetic weight plates to the weight stack.

For example, let's say the weight stack units are 12 pounds, 24, 36, 48, and so on. Once you've mastered 36 pounds, to move immediately to 48 pounds is too much—an increase of a third, which isn't incremental, progressive resistance. But attach two pounds to the 36-pound level, and you have an incremental increase to 38 pounds. Master that, and then move to 40 pounds, and so on. The precise increments will be determined by the available little plates.

Get your own set of fractional plates if where you train doesn't have them. Take them with you when you train.

23. Use accurate weights

Unless you're using calibrated plates you can't be sure you're getting what each plate is supposed to weigh. A bar loaded to 100 pounds may, for example, really be 103 or 97 pounds. Then if you strip that bar down and reload it to 100 pounds using different plates, you're likely to get a different weight than before. Furthermore, the weight excess or discrepancy may be just on one side of the bar, producing an unbalanced barbell.

This is an especially serious matter when you're moving your best weights, and once you're no longer a beginner. An unbalanced or overweight bar may ruin a set and perhaps cause injury, and an underweight bar will give a false sense of progress. When you're using small discs to increase the weight by a pound a week, for example, if your big plates aren't what they seem, you can't be sure you're getting a small overall weight increase relative to the previous workout.

If you have calibrated plates available, use them exclusively. If there are no calibrated plates, at least weigh the big plates so that their actual weights can be discovered.

If this is impossible, manage as best you can—try to discover the plates that are the worst offenders and avoid using them, or find the brand that's the most accurate and stick to that one, or use the same plates and bars every time you train.

24. Never make big changes in training intensity

Make the changes gradually. Sensible, progressive resistance training means increasing training intensity progressively, too.

25. Always warm up well before training hard

The purpose of the general warm-up (for five to ten minutes) that every workout should start with, is to elevate your core temperature, get synovial fluids moving in most of your joints (for lubrication), and probably break you into a sweat (depending on the temperature of the gym). This isn't the same as sweating while being in a hot environment but without exercising.

Following the general warm-up, immediately start strength training. Don't have a break and cool down. Additionally, perform one or more warm-up sets prior to the work set(s) for each exercise—it's better to do too many warm-ups than not enough.

26. Keep your muscles warm

Don't rest excessively between sets and exercises. Warm up properly, and then train at a pace that keeps your muscles warm.

A cool environment but a warm body is what you want. Ideally, the gym temperature should be no higher than 70 degrees Fahrenheit, or 22 degrees Celsius.

27. Develop balanced musculature

If, for example, you work your chest and shoulders hard, but neglect your upper back, or if you train your quadriceps hard but neglect your hamstrings, the imbalanced musculature will increase the risk of injury in the involved muscles and joints.

28. Prepare fully for each set

Check that the weight you've loaded is what you want—consult your training logbook. Add up the total weight of the plates and bar, to check. It's easy to load a barbell, dumbbell, or machine incorrectly.

When you get in position for a set, take the right grip, stance, and body position. Don't rush into a set, grab the bar and then realize after the first rep that you took an imbalanced grip, wrong stance, or are lopsided while on a bench.

29. Use reliable spotters

Spotting—help from one or more assistants—can come from a training partner, or anyone who's in the gym at the time and willing and able to spot you. Good spotting helps in three ways:

a. To assist you with lifting the weight when you can lift it no further, such as when the bar stalls during a bench press ascent.

b. To provide the minimum assistance to ensure that the last rep of a set is done in correct technique. In this case, you probably could get the rep out under your own power, but your technique may break down. A spotter can make the difference between safety or injury.

The first two ways shouldn't apply to beginners, because beginners don't need to train this hard.

c. During a set, you may forget to apply a key point of exercise technique. A knowledgeable spotter could correct this.

Six tips for being a good spotter

Be honest with yourself, and respect your limitations. If you can't spot adequately by yourself, get help.

Be alert, especially when the trainee begins to struggle.

Focus on what the trainee's doing.

Don't injure yourself! While spotting, don't round your back; keep your feet planted—immobile—in a symmetrical way; and stand as close as possible to the bar or dumbbells.

Know the trainee's intentions prior to each set. For example, does he or she need help getting into the starting position?

Keep your hands close to the bar but without interfering with the exercise. When needed, apply assistance with both hands in a symmetrical way. For example, spotting through putting one hand under the center of the bar commonly leads to the bar tipping, as will using two hands asymmetrically.

30. Train on an appropriate surface

Lifting on a wooden or a rubber surface (a level surface, as noted earlier), preferably one that doesn't have concrete directly underneath, is better than training directly on concrete. Wood and rubber are giving, whereas concrete isn't. Wood and rubber reduce the amount of giving that your joints and connective tissues have to tolerate.

Before a set, plant your feet securely, on a non-slip surface.

31. Don't hold your breath

The common tendency, especially when training hard, is to hold your breath during the hard stage of a rep, clench your teeth, and jam your lips together. All of this should be avoided because it increases blood pressure, and may cause blackouts and dizziness. Even if it's for just a split second, a loss of consciousness during training could be disastrous. Although you may not suffer blackouts or dizziness, headaches are a common, immediate result of breath holding during training. And over the long term, breath holding during training encourages varicose veins, and hemorrhoids, because of the damage to vein walls and valves caused by the elevated blood pressure.

A common general rule, while exercising, is to inhale during the brief pause between reps *or* during the negative phase of the movement, and exhale during the positive phase (especially the sticking point). For exercises where there may be a pause for a couple of seconds between reps, inhalation and exhalation may occur during the pause, with the final inhalation taken immediately prior to the start of the next rep.

It's this general rule that's referred to in the technique instruction in this book, but it's not the only way to breathe while strength training. Here's an alternative: Never hold your breath, but focus on the given exercise and muscles being trained, not on your breathing. As long as you're not holding your breath, you'll automatically breathe sufficiently. After some practice you'll find the points during your reps where it's easier to breathe in or out.

When reps are performed slower than about four seconds for each positive or negative phase, it's necessary to breathe *continuously* throughout the reps, and more than once during each phase of a rep.

Not holding your breath also applies out of the gym. Whenever you put forth effort, *exhale*, to avoid elevated blood pressure.

During demanding exercise you won't be able to get enough air through your nose alone. Breathe through your mouth.

To prevent breath holding, *don't close your mouth*. Keep your mouth open—just slightly open will suffice—and your upper and lower teeth apart. It's usually when the lips are jammed together that problems with breath holding occur.

32. Avoid using knee or any other joint wraps

Tight bandages around joints can mask injury problems that are aggravated through training.

33. Avoid pain killers

Don't use pain killers before, during, or after training, as they usually mask problems. Solve problems, don't cover them up and incubate serious injury.

34. Don't wear a lifting belt

Many trainees wear a lifting belt—especially while deadlifting, and squatting—under the misconception that it will protect them from back injuries. And some trainees wear a loose lifting belt throughout their workouts as if it's an item of general clothing.

A loose belt doesn't provide any support. And a tight belt is uncomfortable, can restrict exercise technique, can lead to increased blood pressure, and can only be tolerated for short-duration sets. Powerlifters use lifting belts for singles and low-rep work.

Even if a lifting belt is worn tightly, correct exercise technique is still a necessity for safe training. Wearing a lifting belt can create a false sense of security that encourages the use of incorrect exercise technique. And a tight belt can be harmful in another way because it may permit more weight to be used than would otherwise, which will cause greater injury if exercise technique isn't correct.

Build your own natural belt through a strong corset of muscle. Not wearing a belt *helps* your body to strengthen its core musculature. A lifting belt is a crutch—train without it.

35. Don't be foolish

Many injuries occur because a trainee has given in to bravado. Don't try something you know you're not ready for, and don't try another rep when you know you can't hold correct technique. Never go heavy in an exercise you're not familiar with, or haven't done for a few weeks. Ignore people who encourage you to try something you know is risky. They won't have to live with the consequences of a moment of foolishness, but you will.

For exercises where the weight could pin you, especially the squat and the bench press, *always* use safety bars such as those of a power rack, and ideally a spotter as well. Squat, bench press, and incline bench press stations should incorporate safety bars that the barbell can rest on if you fail on a rep.

36. Keep your wits about you

Don't just be concerned about what you're doing in the gym. Be aware of what's happening around you, and stay clear of danger.

37. Wear appropriate footwear

Shoes with thick, spongy soles and heels may be fine for some activities, but not for strength training. A spongy base won't keep your feet solidly in position. Especially when you're squatting, deadlifting, or overhead pressing, if your feet move just a little, the rest of your body will move, too. It doesn't have to be much movement to throw you out of the correct exercise groove.

But don't train barefoot. Your feet need support while you're training, but it needs to be support of the right kind.

Function comes first in the gym. Get yourself a sturdy pair of shoes with good grip to the floor, arch support, no more than the standard height of heel (and preferably no height difference between the sole and heel), and which minimizes deformation when you're lifting heavy weights. No heel elevation relative to the balls of your feet is especially important when squatting, deadlifting, and leg pressing, because heel elevation increases stress on the knees in those exercises.

Worn shoes can lead to deviations in exercise technique. Discard shoes that have unevenly or excessively worn soles or heels. Ideally, have a pair of shoes solely for gym work that isn't used for other purposes, so that the shoes keep their shape and condition for years. Furthermore, when you train, keep your laces tied tightly.

Even a small change in the size of the heel, or the relative difference between the heel and sole thicknesses of your shoes, can mar your training. This especially applies to the squat and the deadlift, although a change in balance factors can have a negative effect on some other exercises, too.

I recommend the use of orthopedic shoes with molded insoles (including arch support) while training, to compensate for structural or postural instability in the feet, or, in the case of defect-free feet, to maintain existing good condition. Although shoes with custom-made molded insoles are ideal, off-the-shelf shoes with molded insoles are, in most cases, superior to regular shoes. You can even get molded insoles that can be inserted inside your regular footwear, but you may need to remove some of the existing insoles to make room.

38. Concentrate!

Be 100% focused while you train. Never be casual. Furthermore, never turn your head or talk during a set, or pay attention to what anyone's saying other than a spotter who may be giving you technique reminders, or encouragement. Even a slight loss of focus leads to a loss of correct exercise technique, and an increased risk of injury.

All the aforementioned recommendations should be heeded. In addition, there are three *paramount* components of safe, effective strength training:

Controlled rep speed.

Correct exercise technique.

Correct lifting technique when moving equipment.

Rep speed and control

Lift the weight, don't throw it; and lower it, don't drop it. Most trainees perform their reps too fast—typically taking only about one second for each phase of a rep. When doing the exercises described in this book, you should be able to stop each rep at any point, hold the weight briefly, and then *continue*. In an intensive set you may not be able to pause *and* get your target reps, depending on which rep you paused, but the idea is that you *could* pause as a demonstration of control.

Let rep *smoothness* be your guide. If your reps are smooth—including during the transition or turnaround between the positive and negative phases of each rep—you're using the control required for safety and applying stress on the involved musculature. In practice, smooth reps typically take no faster than two to three seconds for the positive phase, and no faster than another two to three seconds for the negative phase. For the positive phase of the final rep of a tough set, when you almost grind to a halt, you may need more than five seconds.

Some exercises have longer strokes or ranges of motion than others, and thus need more seconds to show comparable control. For example, the pulldown has a greater range of motion than the press, the press has a greater range of motion than the bench press, and the bench press has a greater range of motion than the shrug.

It's not necessary to perform reps extremely slowly. Some outlandish claims are sometimes made on behalf of extremely slow training. It's not the best, safest, or "only" way to train. Alone, it can't deliver all the benefits possible from exercise. Extremely slow reps aren't even a guaranteed way to train safely. One of the most persistent injuries I've ever had was sustained while performing extremely slow reps. But I've sustained many injuries while performing reps quickly. Avoid fast reps, but there's no need to move to the other extreme.

The first few reps of a work set don't require the degree of effort that the final reps do. As you fatigue, you need to increase your effort level. If you apply your full effort at the start of a set, the weight will move explosively and without the smooth control required for safe training. But toward the end of a set, once you're training hard, you'll *need* to apply your full effort in order to complete the reps. Apply *only* as much effort as you need to complete each rep with the required control.

The use of smooth, controlled rep speed is essential for safe training. Never use fast or jerky movements.

Smooth, controlled reps can, however, be performed with correct *or* incorrect exercise technique. Even if a smooth, controlled rep speed is used, if it's combined with incorrect exercise technique it will produce high-risk training.

For safe training, a smooth, controlled rep speed must be *combined* with correct exercise technique. Exercise technique is concerned with equipment set-up, grip, stance, body positioning, and bar pathways. Although rep speed and exercise technique are two separate issues, they are integral parts of safe training.

Some elite bodybuilders, lifters, and athletes can tolerate and even prosper on explosive training because they have the required robustness of joints, and connective tissue. But even they often pay a heavy price in terms of injuries, eventually. There's no need to take any risk with explosive training. A slower and controlled rep speed—as promoted in this book—is much safer, and by far the best option for typical trainees. Why risk pushing your body beyond its structural limits, and possibly suffering permanent injuries, when there are safer ways to train that are highly effective?

The four main grips

Pronated grip

One of the most popular grips, used in many exercises. When your hands are at your sides, a pronated grip has your knuckles facing to the front, and palms facing to the rear. When your hands are overhead, the grip has your knuckles facing to the rear, and palms to the front.

Supinated grip

Another of the most popular grips, used in many exercises. When your hands are at your sides, a supinated grip has your knuckles facing to the rear, and palms facing to the front. When your hands are overhead, the supinated grip has your knuckles facing to the front, and your palms facing to the rear.

Parallel grip

A grip that has the palms parallel with each other.

Reverse grip

A grip where a bar is held with one hand pronated and the other supinated. It's a specialized grip for a small number of exercises, such as the deadlift. It's also called an *alternating grip*, or *mixed grip*.

Four different grips: left, pronated grip (two views); middle, supinated grip (two views); top right, parallel grip; bottom right, mixed or reverse grip.

A primer on anatomy

To understand the muscle involvement in each exercise you need at least a rudimentary knowledge of the names and functions of the main muscles of the human body, as outlined in this chapter. Most of the deep, hidden muscles have been excluded, however, because of the complexity of the entire system. For example, there are many deep muscles in the back, between and around the vertebrae.

But first you need to know the basics of the skeleton.

The skeletal system

The bones comprise the framework to which the muscles are attached. There are 206 bones in the human body, including 28 in the skull. These are arranged into a cranial group (eight bones), facial group (14 bones), and the three tiny bones in each ear (the auditory ossicles).

The skeleton is divided into two regions: The axial skeleton consists of 80 bones and is comprised of the skull, spine, and thorax (ribs and sternum). The appendicular skeleton consists of 126 bones and is comprised of the shoulder girdle, pelvis, and limbs.

Most of the bones of the skeleton are joined to one another by movable joints, or articulations.

The toes (14 phalanges) articulate with the five metatarsals (the framework of the instep), which articulate with the tarsus (seven tarsal bones of the ankle, including the calcaneus, or heel bone). The talus— uppermost tarsal—is the primary bone of the ankle joint. The ankle joint articulates with the distal ends of the fibula and tibia (shinbone).

The proximal ends of the fibula and tibia articulate with the distal end of the femur (thighbone), at the knee.

The proximal end of the femur articulates with the pelvic girdle (hip bones), which in turn articulates solidly with the sacrum of the vertebral column. The pelvic girdle supports the weight of the upper body, and distributes it to the lower limbs.

The torso is connected to the vertebral column through the rib cage (12 pairs of ribs, and the sternum).

The vertebral column has 33 or 34 bones in a child, but because of fusions that occur later in the lower spine, there are usually 26 separate bones in the adult vertebral column. The skull is attached to the top of the vertebral column at the first vertebra, called the atlas.

Above and to the rear of the rib cage, are the pectoral or shoulder girdles (a clavicle or collar bone, and a scapula or shoulder blade, for each girdle). Each shoulder articulates with the proximal end of the humerus.

The distal end of the humerus articulates, via the elbow, with the proximal ends of the ulna and radius. The distal end of the radius articulates with the wrist.

The hand, or manus, is composed of the wrist, or carpus (eight small, oval-like bones called the carpals), the metacarpus (five metacarpals), and the phalanges (or fingers, comprised of 14 bones in each hand).

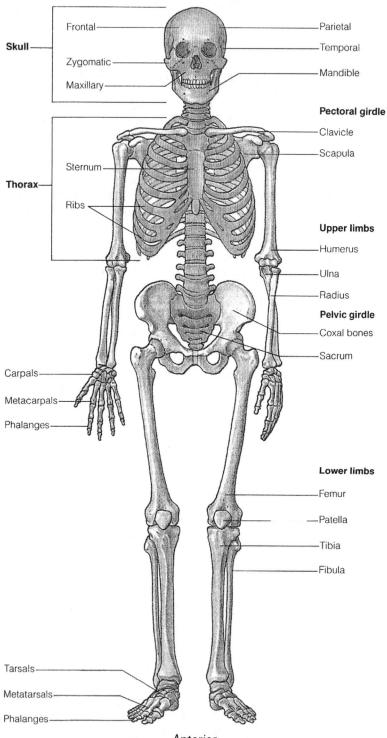

Skull — Frontal — Parietal

Zygomatic — Temporal

Maxillary — Mandible

Pectoral girdle

Clavicle

Scapula

Thorax — Sternum

Ribs

Upper limbs

Humerus

Ulna

Radius

Pelvic girdle

Coxal bones

Sacrum

Carpals

Metacarpals

Phalanges

Lower limbs

Femur

Patella

Tibia

Fibula

Tarsals

Metatarsals

Phalanges

Anterior

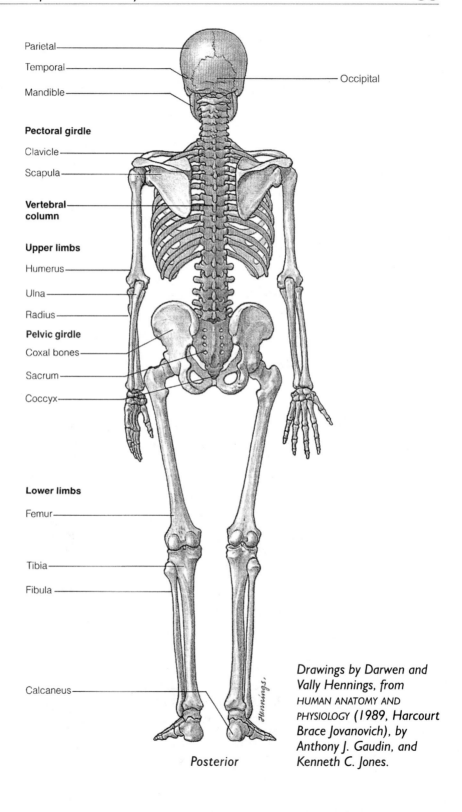

Parietal

Temporal

Mandible

Occipital

Pectoral girdle

Clavicle

Scapula

Vertebral column

Upper limbs

Humerus

Ulna

Radius

Pelvic girdle

Coxal bones

Sacrum

Coccyx

Lower limbs

Femur

Tibia

Fibula

Calcaneus

Posterior

Drawings by Darwen and Vally Hennings, from HUMAN ANATOMY AND PHYSIOLOGY *(1989, Harcourt Brace Jovanovich), by Anthony J. Gaudin, and Kenneth C. Jones.*

The main musculature

There are more than 600 muscles that move the skeleton and some soft tissues, such as the lips and eyelids. Movement is produced by contraction and relaxation of opposing muscle groups, at joints.

Calf muscles

Group of seven posterior muscles below the knee, divided into superficial and deep groups, whose functions include extending the ankle (pointing the toes). The two main muscles are the meaty two-headed gastrocnemius and, beneath it, the soleus. The gastrocnemius connects the heel to the femur, and the soleus connects the heel to the tibia and fibula—the gastrocnemius crosses the ankle *and* knee joints, while the soleus crosses the ankle joint only. The tendons of these two muscles, together with the plantaris, fuse to form the Achilles tendon.

Exercises that train the calves are calf raises.

Other muscles below the knee

There are four anterior muscles, which move the toes and foot—the largest is the tibialis anterior, which runs alongside the tibia. And two muscles extend along the lateral surface of the fibula—peroneus longus, and peroneus brevis, which lower and evert the foot.

Hamstrings

The three muscles of the rear thigh: biceps femoris (two-headed muscle), semitendinosus, and semimembranosus. They flex the knees, and contribute to hip extension (rearward movement of the femur). The hamstrings are abbreviated to *hams*.

The primary exercise that trains the hamstrings is the leg curl. Deadlifts, squats, leg press, and back extensions also work the hamstrings.

Quadriceps femoris

Group of four muscles of the frontal thigh: rectus femoris, vastus lateralis, vastus medialis, and vastus intermedius. The tendons of insertion of the four quadriceps muscles form the patella tendon.

The rectus femoris connects the tibia (through the patella) to the pelvis, whereas the other three connect the tibia (through the patella) to the femur. The rectus femoris flexes the femur (raises it) at the hip joint *and* extends the leg at the knee joint; the other three quadriceps muscles extend the leg only. The quadriceps are abbreviated to *quads*.

Exercises that train the quadriceps include squats, parallel-grip deadlift, and leg press.

Sartorius

The longest muscle in the body, which runs diagonally across the frontal thigh, from the proximal end of the tibia, to the outer edge of the pelvic girdle. The sartorius flexes the femur, and rotates the femur laterally.

Adductors, thigh

There are five major adductors of the femur, in the inner thigh: pectineus, adductor longus, adductor brevis, adductor magnus, and gracilis. They connect the pelvis to the femur, except for the gracilis that connects the pelvis to the tibia. They are responsible for adduction, flexion, and lateral rotation of the femur.

Squats, and the leg press, work the thigh adductors. A wider stance increases adductor involvement.

Buttocks

The muscular masses posterior to the pelvis formed by the three gluteal muscles (*glutes*): gluteus maximus, gluteus medius, and gluteus minimus. They extend (move rearward), rotate, and abduct the femur. (A group of six smaller muscles beneath the buttocks rotates the femur laterally.)

Exercises that train the buttocks include squats, deadlifts, and leg press.

Iliopsoas

The single name for three muscles—iliacus, psoas major, psoas minor—that fuse into a single tendon on the femur. These muscles originate on the pelvis or on some of the lower vertebrae, and are hidden from view. They flex the femur, and rotate it laterally. They are called the *hip flexors*. (Another hip flexor is the rectus femoris, of the quadriceps.)

The hip flexors are worked by most abdominal exercises.

Some of the musculature shown on the right side of each anatomy chart is different from that shown on the left. This occurs where the outer layer of muscle has been omitted in order to show some of the deeper musculature.

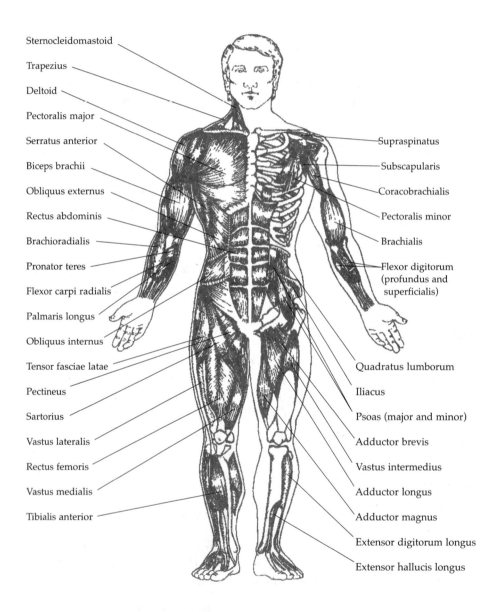

Sternocleidomastoid
Trapezius
Deltoid
Pectoralis major
Serratus anterior
Biceps brachii
Obliquus externus
Rectus abdominis
Brachioradialis
Pronator teres
Flexor carpi radialis
Palmaris longus
Obliquus internus
Tensor fasciae latae
Pectineus
Sartorius
Vastus lateralis
Rectus femoris
Vastus medialis
Tibialis anterior

Supraspinatus
Subscapularis
Coracobrachialis
Pectoralis minor
Brachialis
Flexor digitorum (profundus and superficialis)
Quadratus lumborum
Iliacus
Psoas (major and minor)
Adductor brevis
Vastus intermedius
Adductor longus
Adductor magnus
Extensor digitorum longus
Extensor hallucis longus

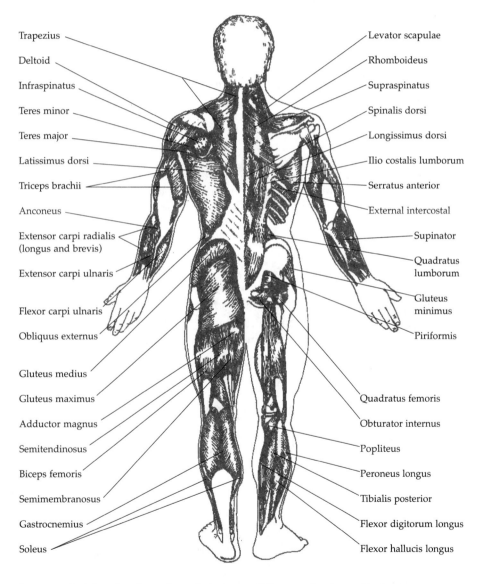

Trapezius

Deltoid

Infraspinatus

Teres minor

Teres major

Latissimus dorsi

Triceps brachii

Anconeus

Extensor carpi radialis
(longus and brevis)

Extensor carpi ulnaris

Flexor carpi ulnaris

Obliquus externus

Gluteus medius

Gluteus maximus

Adductor magnus

Semitendinosus

Biceps femoris

Semimembranosus

Gastrocnemius

Soleus

Levator scapulae

Rhomboideus

Supraspinatus

Spinalis dorsi

Longissimus dorsi

Ilio costalis lumborum

Serratus anterior

External intercostal

Supinator

Quadratus
lumborum

Gluteus
minimus

Piriformis

Quadratus femoris

Obturator internus

Popliteus

Peroneus longus

Tibialis posterior

Flexor digitorum longus

Flexor hallucis longus

Drawings by Eleni Lambrou, based on those of Chartex Products, England.

Erector spinae

Large muscles of the vertebral column—the iliocostalis, longissimus, and spinalis groups—that stabilize the spine, extend it (arch the back), and move the spine from side to side. Some of the muscles produce rotation, too. They are abbreviated to *erectors*, and are also called the *sacrospinalis*.

Squats, deadlifts, and back extensions train the erector spinae.

Multifidii

Large muscle group deep to the erector spinae, from the sacrum to the neck, which extends and rotates the vertebral column.

The multifidus group is worked by the rotary torso, twisting crunch, and the same exercises that train the erector spinae.

Rectus abdominis

The frontal, "six-pack" muscle of the abdominal wall, connecting the pelvis to the lower ribs. It compresses the abdomen, and flexes the trunk. The rectus abdominis is abbreviated to *abs*.

Exercises that train the rectus abdominis include variations of the crunch.

Obliques

The two muscles at the sides of the abdominal wall—external abdominal oblique, and internal abdominal oblique—connecting the ribs with the pelvis. They compress the abdomen, and flex and rotate the trunk.

Exercises that train this muscle include side bends, and crunches.

Transversus abdominis

Deep muscle of the abdominal wall, beneath the rectus abdominis, and obliques. It compresses the abdomen, and flexes the trunk.

Exercises that train this muscle include variations of the crunch.

Quadratus lumborum

Deep muscle either side of the lower spine that helps form the rear of the abdominal wall. Unlike the other muscles of the abdominal wall, the quadratus lumborum doesn't compress the abdomen; instead, it depresses the ribs. When one side acts alone, it bends the spine to the side; when the two sides act together, they extend the spine.

Exercises that train this muscle include side bends, and back extensions.

Serratus anterior

The muscle on the rib cage underneath and slightly forward of the armpit, which gives a ridged appearance on a lean body. It protracts and rotates the scapula.

Pectoralis major

The large muscle of the chest connecting the chest and clavicle to the humerus. It adducts, flexes, and medially rotates the humerus. The pectorals are abbreviated to *pecs*.

Exercises that train the pecs include bench presses, and parallel bar dips.

Pectoralis minor

The muscle beneath the pectoralis major, connecting some ribs to the scapula. It protracts the scapula, and elevates the ribs.

Latissimus dorsi

The large, wing-like back muscle that connects the humerus to the lower vertebrae and pelvic girdle. It adducts, extends, and medially rotates the humerus. These muscles are abbreviated to *lats*.

Exercises that train the latissimus dorsi include the machine pullover, pulldown, and rows.

Rhomboids

The rhomboideus major and rhomboideus minor, which connect some of the upper vertebrae to the scapula. They retract and rotate the scapula.

Exercises that train the rhomboids include the pulldown, and rows.

Rotator cuff muscles

The rotator cuff is where the tendons of four small muscles in the upper back and shoulder area—supraspinatus, infraspinatus, teres minor, and subscapularis—fuse with the tissues of the shoulder joint. The rotator cuff muscles—or *articular* muscles of the shoulder—are involved in abduction, adduction, and rotation of the humerus.

The external rotators are usually neglected, and are trained by the L-fly.

Trapezius

The large, kite-shaped muscle that connects the skull, scapulae, clavicles, and some upper vertebrae. It retracts, elevates, depresses and rotates the scapula, and extends the head (moves it rearward). The trapezius is abbreviated to *traps*.

Exercises that train the trapezius include shrugs, rows, and the deadlift and its variations. The neck extension works the upper traps.

Sternocleidomastoid

The muscle at the sides of the neck, connecting the sternum and clavicles to the skull. Acting together, both sides of the sterno-cleidomastoid flex the head and neck; when acting separately, each muscle produces rotation and lateral flexion.

The four-way neck machine is the preferred exercise for this muscle.

Deltoid

The shoulder cap muscle, and a prime mover of the humerus—it abducts, flexes, extends, and rotates the humerus. It has three heads: anterior, medial, and posterior. The deltoids are abbreviated to *delts*.

Exercises that train the deltoids include the dumbbell press, barbell press, and lateral raise.

Biceps brachii

The two-headed muscle (long, and short heads) of the front or anterior surface of the arm, which connects the upper scapula to the radius and forearm muscle, and flexes the forearm and thus the elbow joint, and supinates the forearm. The biceps are abbreviated to *bis*.

Exercises that train the biceps include curls, pulldown, and rows.

Brachialis

The muscle of the front of the arm beneath the biceps, which connects the humerus to the ulna, and flexes the forearm and elbow joint.

Exercises that train the brachialis include curls, pulldown, and rows.

Triceps brachii

The three-headed muscle (long, medial, and lateral heads) on the rear or posterior surface of the arm, which connects the humerus and scapula to the ulna, and extends the forearm (and the elbow joint). Just the long head of the triceps adducts the arm. The triceps are abbreviated to *tris*.

Exercises that train the triceps include bench presses, presses, parallel bar dips, and the pushdown.

Forearms

The anterior surface (palm side) has eight muscles spread over three layers, most of which are involved in flexing the wrist and fingers. The posterior surface has ten muscles spread over two layers, involved in extending the wrist and moving the fingers.

Timed hold, deadlifts, shrugs, grippers, rows, pulldown, and finger extension train the forearms, along with all exercises that work the grip.

PART 2

How to master exercise technique

1. Back extension	basic back extension	54
	45-degree back extension	57
	spinal extension	57
	machine back extension	58
2. Bench press	barbell bench press	60
	dumbbell bench press	68
	close-grip bench press	72
	incline barbell bench press	76
	incline dumbbell bench press	80
3. Calf raise	standing two-legged calf raise	84
	standing one-legged calf raise	86
4. Chin-up (and pull-up)		88
5. Crunch	basic crunch	94
	modified basic crunch	96
	machine crunch	97
	reverse crunch	98
	twisting crunch	100
6. Curl	seated dumbbell curl	104
	incline dumbbell curl	105
	barbell curl	106
	hammer curl	107
7. Deadlift	deadlift (conventional deadlift)	112
	parallel-grip deadlift	122
	partial deadlift	130
	sumo deadlift	134
8. Finger extension		136
9. Hand-gripper work	torsion-spring gripper	139
	Ivanko super gripper	141
10. Lateral raise	dumbbell lateral raise	144
	machine lateral raise	145
11. Leg curl		146
12. Leg press		150
13. L-fly		156

14. Neck work   manual resistance neck work   161
                    four-way neck machine   162

15. Parallel bar dip   164

16. Press   seated barbell press   168
              seated dumbbell press   172

17. Pulldown   176

18. Pullover   machine pullover   180
               breathing pullover   184

19. Pushdown   186

20. Rotary torso   188

21. Row   one-arm dumbbell row   190
           cable row   192
           seated machine row   196
           prone low-incline dumbbell row   197

22. Shrug   198

23. Side bend   dumbbell side bend   203
             pulley side bend   205

24. Squat   squat (conventional or back squat)   212
           front squat   230
           ball squat   240
           hip-belt squat   244

25. Timed hold   250

Supplementary exercises
    26. Grip machine training   254
    27. Lever bar work   256
    28. Overhead lockout   258
    29. Pinch-grip lifting   262
    30. Rader chest pull   266
    31. Wrist roller training   268

How to master exercise technique

Properly done, weight-lifting is safe, but the use of correct exercise technique is the exception in nearly all gyms. Gyms are usually terrible places for learning correct exercise technique. Few trainees practice correct technique because hardly anyone knows what it is, and this includes most gym instructors, and personal trainers. Exercise technique isn't secondary to program design, and training intensity. Technique comes first!

Exercise technique isn't simple. It requires detailed instruction, and serious study, if you're to master it. Make *correct exercise technique* your number one training motto. Make no compromises, *ever*.

All strength-training exercises aren't included here, for three reasons:

1. The most effective exercises are limited in number.

2. Many of the excluded exercises are inferior to the selected ones.

3. Effective strength training for typical trainees is built around short routines.

Some exercises don't produce acute injury but an accumulation of damage that, over time, causes chronic injury. Just because an exercise doesn't hurt you today, next week, or next month, doesn't mean that it won't hurt you later.

When I was a beginner I had little or no time for anyone who talked or wrote about the possible dangers of training. Being a teenager I could, at first, get away with foolish training methods without much immediate discomfort. Therefore I continued with harmful practices that included squatting with my heels raised on a board and the barbell too high on my shoulders, hack machine squatting, Smith machine squatting, bench pressing with a wide grip and to my upper chest, round-back deadlifting, explosive lifting, and specific cheating movements. A few years later I was plagued with serious injuries, especially to my knees and back. Countless trainees have experienced similar problems.

I sustained most of my training injuries because I used incorrect exercise technique. And the remaining injuries were caused because I didn't apply what's taught in Part I of this book.

All these injuries would have been avoided had I applied everything that this book teaches.

The ESSENTIAL factor of individuality

Even if exercise technique is correct, rep speed is controlled, and the handling of weights is faultless while setting up equipment, an exercise can still cause problems if, for a given individual, training is excessive in terms of frequency or volume, or if the adding of weight to the bar is rushed.

For instance, perhaps you're not a beginner, and you're squatting and deadlifting two times per week, your exercise technique is correct, rep speed is controlled, and your training volume is low, yet your lower back and knees still don't feel right. But when you were a beginner, there was no problem with this training frequency. Now, because of the increased training load, the situation has changed. A change to deadlifting and squatting just once a week each, on the same day, will give more recovery time, and your knees and lower back may start to feel fine again. You may still be able to train your lower back two times a week, but make it the back extension at the second session. And you may still be able to train your thighs two times a week, but make it the leg press at the second session, for example.

With exercise technique, what's "safe" can be an individual matter. Age, body structure and proportions, and any past injuries, among other factors, may turn what's generally a safe exercise into a potentially harmful one.

Study this book to learn about correct exercise technique, and then apply it *consistently*. If, however, despite using *correct technique*, along with a *controlled* rep speed, *gradual* increases in progressive resistance, *abbreviated* training routines, and *adequate* recovery time between workouts, you *still* experience joint or soft tissue irritation from a given exercise, substitute it with a comparable exercise.

Apply the first imperative of exercise: "Do no harm."

Free-weights, and machines

With a barbell and dumbbell set you can do the same exercises anywhere in the world. Free-weights are almost universal in gyms, but good machinery isn't. The technique instruction for exercises that use free-weights is the same for all brands of that gear, but not so for machinery where, for example, the instructions for one brand's squat machine are different from another's. As a result of these factors, and others, free-weights are given priority in this book.

If, however, you have access to the generally good machinery—for example, Body Masters, Cybex, Hammer Strength, MedX, and Nautilus—you could substitute it for the comparable free-weights exercises; but tread carefully because even some of the generally good machines can cause irritations and injuries for some trainees even when those machines are used correctly. And most machines can't accommodate all body sizes. Of course, exercises that use free-weights can also cause problems, especially if they aren't performed correctly.

A machine exercise may cause irritation, but the comparable free-weights exercise may not, and vice versa, depending on the individual and the exercise concerned.

Features of good machinery include smoothness of motion, ease of entry and exit, and the ability to accommodate a variety of body types (through adjustment of seats, back pads, and movement arms).

Although high-tech machinery can be useful, it's not essential. Free-weights alone, properly used, have proven to be tremendously effective.

General note regarding machines

Various manufacturers produce variations on the same basic machine designs. One manufacturer's pullover machine, for example, may produce an effective upper-body exercise, whereas another version may be a source of joint irritation.

Whenever you use a machine, follow the manufacturer's guidelines—which are often fixed to the machines themselves. The correct set-up position is essential. For instance, on a shoulder machine, you may need to line up your shoulder joints with the pivot points.

Fine-tune your set-up until you find what feels most comfortable. You may need several workouts. A set-up that initially felt awkward may, after some adjustment, feel fine. Never push hard on a machine until after you've found a set-up that's proven safe for several workouts, without producing any negative reaction.

Personal coaching

Don't assume that anyone who claims to be a qualified personal trainer knows what he's doing. Strings of letters that indicate certifications of various organizations, or degrees obtained, don't necessarily signify competence as a coach. Be on your guard.

To determine whether someone can help you to improve your technique, watch the trainer at work. Although the following checklist isn't entirely to do with exercise technique, the non-technique components reflect on overall ability as a trainer.

1. Is the technique taught like that described in this book?

2. Does the trainer remind his charge of key technique points before an exercise, and in the course of it?

3. Has the trainer modified his client's exercise selection and technique according to any physical limitations the trainee may have?

4. Does the trainer keep accurate records of weight and reps for every work set?

5. Does the trainer consult his client's training log before each set, to ensure that the correct weight is loaded?

6. Is the trainer attentive, supportive, and respectful?

7. Does the trainer keep his charge's mind focused on the work at hand?

If the trainer doesn't score well on all these points, look elsewhere. If the trainer scores well on these points but the deadlift, squat, and other major movements weren't done in the workout you inspected, ask the trainer to demonstrate how he teaches those movements. Compare his instruction with what's described in this book. If the differences are more than minor, look elsewhere.

Joining a local powerlifting club, or attending occasionally, may help. A savvy coach from the club should be able to provide technique tips.

Once you know about correct exercise technique, teach an observer what to look for to provide feedback to help you improve your technique. Alternatively, use a video camera and record your technique, for analysis later. A video camera can be an outstanding tool to help you to improve your exercise technique.

Units of measurement

Imperial and metric units are used interchangeably in this book. An inch is about two and a half centimeters, four inches is about ten centimeters, and a foot is about 30 centimeters. A pound is about 0.45 kilogram, and about 2.2 pounds comprise one kilogram.

Technical accuracy

Throughout this book, strict anatomical definitions of arm, forearm, thigh, and leg are used. This means avoiding ambiguous terms such as *lower leg, upper leg, lower arm,* or *upper arm,* and not using *arm* and *leg* to encompass undetermined portions of the upper and lower extremities respectively. The leg is the portion between the foot and the knee, the thigh is the portion between the knee and the hip, the forearm is the portion between the hand and the elbow, and the arm is the portion between the elbow and the shoulder.

The word *flex* is used in this book only as the opposite of *extend*. Flex is commonly used to mean *make tense* but *without* flexion.

Important breathing guidelines

A common general rule while exercising is to inhale during the pause between reps, or during the negative phase of the movement, and exhale during the positive phase. For exercises where there may be a pause between reps, inhalation *and* exhalation may occur during the pause, with the final inhalation taken immediately prior to the start of the next rep. It's this guideline that's usually referred to in the technique instruction in this book, but it's not the only way to breathe while strength training.

Here's an alternative guideline: While never holding your breath, focus on the given exercise and muscles being trained, *not* your breathing. As long as you're not holding your breath, you'll automatically breathe sufficiently. To prevent breath holding, *don't close your mouth.*

When reps are performed very slowly—slower than about four seconds for each positive or negative phase—it's necessary to breathe continuously throughout each rep, perhaps with more than one inhalation-exhalation cycle during each phase of a rep.

Dumbbell training

Some trainees prefer dumbbells to barbells in upper-body exercises because the dumbbells allow more flexibility with wrist positioning, and thus permit more comfortable training.

Books on strength training and bodybuilding usually provide skimpy descriptions of exercise technique. But exercise technique isn't a simple matter. The exercises need to be described in detail.

Photographs alone can't show all the details of exercise technique. Please study all of the written instructions.

The photographs are for illustration purposes only. In some cases, the models didn't wear shirts so that the involved musculature or back positioning could be seen clearly. And spotters and safety set-up considerations aren't illustrated other than in a few specific photographs. When YOU train, wear a shirt, and fully attend to all safety considerations, as described in the text.

I. BACK EXTENSION

Main muscles worked

lower back, quadratus lumborum, multifidii, buttocks, hamstrings (the latter two muscle groups are especially heavily worked in back extensions that use conventional apparatus)

The multifidus muscle group is deep to the erector spinae, from the sacrum to the neck, and extends and rotates the vertebral column.

Capsule description

flex and extend your torso while keeping your legs fixed

The basic or conventional back extension, often called a *hyperextension*, has your legs fixed and your torso moves into line with them. In the *reverse* back extension, your torso is fixed and your legs move into line with it. The reverse back extension is a valuable exercise but it doesn't provide the spinal flexion and extension of the conventional back extension, and the special apparatus required isn't commonly available. Therefore, the reverse back extension isn't included in this book.

Done correctly, back extensions involve safe flexion (or rounding) of the spine, and extension (or straightening) of the spine, whereas deadlifts, done correctly, primarily involve static contraction of the spinal erectors. For safety, deadlifts should *never* be performed with a rounded back.

The back extension strengthens the lower back in a way that deadlifts may not, because of the spinal *extension* of the former. The back extension may even strengthen some muscles of the lower back that deadlifts can't. Back extensions aren't, however, a substitute for deadlifts unless you're unable to do any form of deadlift safely. When compared, deadlifts are whole-body exercises, whereas back extensions affect limited musculature.

For most trainees, back extensions and deadlifts are complementary, and correct use of both will produce the best overall results.

Basic back extension

A purpose-built apparatus is available in many gyms for the basic back extension.

Rest your upper thighs on the support pad, and your heels or calves against the rearmost support. With your hands on the floor, find the position so that the front edge of the support pad doesn't hurt your groin. You may need additional padding over that edge. If the apparatus has adjustable components, fine-tune them for thigh and groin comfort.

Keep your knees slightly bent, to avoid exaggerated stress on them.

With your head and torso hanging vertically, cross your forearms on your chest. Raise your torso in a

The top photograph shows a partially extended neck. In this exercise, maintain a neutral neck—neither extended, nor flexed.

slow, smooth, controlled, symmetrical fashion until your torso is parallel with the floor, or just above parallel. Hold the top position for two seconds.

As you return to the starting position, gradually round (flex) your spine. Pause for a second at the bottom, then slowly and smoothly start the next rep. Rounding the spine on the descent, and then extending or straightening it on the ascent, are required for the best effect.

This exercise is commonly done with the hands behind the head, or with a plate held behind the head. Both place unnecessary strain on the neck and cervical vertebrae. Keep your forearms crossed on your chest, and hold a plate or dumbbell to your chest when extra resistance is needed.

Inhale at the bottom position or during the descent, and exhale during the ascent; or, just breathe freely—*don't* hold your breath. You may need multiple breaths per rep.

Apparatus improvisation

If you don't have access to a purpose-built apparatus for the back extension, or a machine, try an old-fashioned way. Elevate a horizontal bench on crates or boxes. Place your thighs on the bench, face down, and put your hands on the floor. Find the precise position on the bench that's comfortable. Have an assistant hold you down, at your calves. You may need a folded towel under your knees, and over the edge of the bench, for padding. Then perform the basic back extension.

Alternatively, position a bench or board over the pins in a power rack, set at the appropriate height to permit a full range of motion at the bottom of the exercise. The bench or board must be secured in position so that it can't slide off the pins during use. Furthermore, jam the rear of the bench or board between a pair of pins, so that it can't come out of position during a set. Use a belt to strap your legs to the bench.

In both cases, experiment to find the position to be held or strapped to the bench that's comfortable for your knees. Avoid compression of your kneecaps.

The 45-degree back extension

This is an alternative to the basic back extension. Exercise the same control, flexion, and extension as in the basic back extension, and the same method of holding resistance. To bring your torso into line with your legs in the 45-degree back extension, your back has to come up to above parallel with the floor.

Generally, the 45-degree back extension provides greater muscular loading at the bottom of the movement, while the basic version provides greater loading at the top.

Spinal extension

Using the set-ups for the basic and 45-degree back extensions, spinal extension *alone* is possible if technique is modified as illustrated on the right. This yields a shortened overall range of motion relative to traditional back extensions, but focuses the work on the spinal musculature. In traditional back extensions there's back *and* hip extension. For back or spinal extension *alone*, keep your lower vertebrae fixed throughout, and move only your middle and upper vertebrae. Practice is required before this technique can be mastered.

Machine back extension

Back extension machines are also called *lower-back* or *lumbar-extension* machines. Different brands have different designs, and the effectiveness for the lumbar musculature varies. The MedX lumbar-extension machine is probably the premier one. Because of their design and use, some back extension machines provide little or no meaningful exercise for the lumbar musculature.

To be maximally effective for working the lumbar musculature, a back extension machine *must* fully restrain the body in four locations: feet, knees, thighs, and pelvis. The feet are restrained by a foot board. The knees are restrained by a belt or bar. The thighs are restrained by a belt strapped tightly over the upper thighs. The pelvis is restrained by a pad that's positioned against the rear of the hips. (Some machines may have head rests, too.)

If any of these four restraints are absent, or not correctly employed, you'll increase the involvement of your hamstrings and muscles of your hips, but reduce the involvement of your lumbar-extension muscles. For best effect on your lumbar musculature, there must be no movement of your legs, thighs, or pelvis. The muscles of your legs, thighs, and hips contract, but the restraints prevent these muscles contributing substantial force to the movement.

It's also essential that you don't involve your hands. Cross your hands on your chest. Furthermore, it's critical that you use a controlled rep speed, and a safe range of motion.

Follow the manufacturer's set-up guidelines, and fine-tune to suit you.

In the starting position, flex (round) your back moderately. Then as you extend your back, gradually straighten and then slightly arch your back. Don't exaggerate the arch. Move smoothly at all times, including the turnaround points of each rep.

Take at least three seconds for the positive phase of the rep; pause for a second at the extended, fully contracted position, with your scapulae fully retracted; and then take at least a further three seconds for the negative phase, while gradually rounding your back. Pause for a second in the starting position, then smoothly move into the next rep.

Use as full a range of motion as is safe for you. At first, don't try the maximum degree of (forward) flexion or (rearward) extension.

Start with minimal resistance, and very low intensity of effort. Only after you know the maximum safe range of motion for you—after perhaps a couple of weeks use—should you start to increase resistance and effort levels *gradually*. You may find that your flexibility increases during the first few weeks of use, and permits a greater safe range of motion. *But even when you've fully adapted to the machine back extension, don't work it until muscular exhaustion because that may cause injury.* Train each work set hard, but *not* until your limit.

Be especially careful if you have had any back injuries.

Don't try to maintain a flat back in the back extension. It's important that the spine flexes and extends, that is, rounds and arches moderately. Without this flexion and extension, the lumbar musculature won't be fully stimulated.

Progression in back extensions

The 45-degree back extension may be a good introduction to back extensions if you don't have sufficient strength to perform the basic version for the required reps, and don't have access to a back extension machine. (A back extension machine can be used with little or no resistance, but the basic and 45-degree back extensions have the minimum resistance of the weight of your torso.) Graduate to the basic back extension after two to three months on the 45-degree version.   If the 45-degree back extension is currently too difficult, use the back extension while on the floor, without equipment. Once you can perform 20 controlled, smooth floor back extensions with your arms extended, elbows straight, and a pause at the top of each rep, progress to another form of the back extension. Try the 45-degree back extension, or, if the set-up for that exercise isn't available, try the basic back extension.

If you have access to the basic and 45-degree back extensions, do a single work set of each rather than two sets of only one of them. Alternatively, use the machine back extension.

2. BENCH PRESS

Five forms of the bench press will be described:
   barbell bench press
   dumbbell bench press
   close-grip bench press
   incline barbell bench press
   incline dumbbell bench press

Barbell bench press

Main muscles worked

pectorals, deltoids, triceps

Capsule description

lie on your back, bar in your hands, arms vertical, elbows locked; lower the bar to your chest, then push it up

Set-up

This exercise is done supine, lying on your back on a horizontal bench. Use a straight barbell, not one with bends or cambers in it. Bench press inside a four-post power rack with pins and saddles correctly positioned, and securely in place.

Alternatively, bench press between sturdy squat stands together with spotter (or safety) bars or racks, or use a half rack, or use a combination bench-and-weight-stands unit together with spotter bars. Some bench-and-stands units have built-in, adjustable spotter bars. Set the safety bars at the appropriate height, and position yourself on the bench so you won't miss the safety bars if you need to set the barbell on them.

If there are no spotter or safety bars to stop the bar getting stuck on your chest if you fail on a rep, you must have an alert and strong spotter in attendance.

Center a sturdy, stable bench between the weight supports. In a power rack, if possible, mark where the bench should be, to be centered. Use a tape measure to ensure correct centering. The rack and bench should be level—have them checked, and corrected if necessary.

Depending on the bench press unit you use, the bar saddles may be adjustable. Position them neither too high, nor too low.

A combination bench-and-weight-stands unit, but without spotter bars. An assistant must be used as a spotter with this type of unit. There's a raised platform here for the spotter to stand on, for easier handling of the barbell by the spotter. An unloaded barbell is shown resting across the unit's upper bar saddles.

Positioning on the bench

Position yourself on the bench so that you won't hit the uprights of the rack or stands with the bar during the bench press ascent, but also so that you minimize the horizontal movement of the bar during the unracking and racking of the bar. The bar, when racked, may, for example, be directly above your nose. The set-up varies according to individual body structure, height of the bar holders, and depth of the saddles. Experiment with a bare bar, to find what works best for you. Make a note of where your eyes are, relative to the bar, when you're on the bench with the bar in the saddles, ready to unrack the bar to start a set.

Lie on the bench with your feet, hips, back, and head all in position. Your heels should be on an imaginary vertical line drawn from your knees, or slightly in front of it. If your heels are behind this line (that is, pulled toward your pelvis) that will lead to exaggerated arching of your lower back. Avoid that. Although some arching in the lower back is normal, don't exaggerate it. Some trainees exaggerate the arch, to raise their chests as much as possible in order to reduce the distance the bar has to move before it touches their chests, to increase the weights they use. This technique has injured many trainees.

Establish a strong base, with your feet flat on the floor wider than shoulder width. Don't place your feet close together on the floor, and don't place them on the bench in any manner—both placements would reduce your stability. Never lift your heels off the floor during the bench press. If you have short lower limbs and can't keep your feet flat on the floor, raise your feet a few inches using low blocks, or plates stacked smooth side up.

Set the rack's pins, or whatever safety bars you use, an inch below the height of your inflated chest when you're in position on the bench. A length of hose or tubing may be put over each safety bar, to soften contact

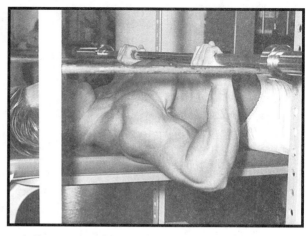

with the barbell. If you fail on a rep, lower the bar to your chest, exhale, and set the bar on the supports.

Grip

While the bar is at the line of your lower pecs, your hand spacing should put your forearms in a vertical position when viewed (by an assistant) from the side and from your feet. Your elbows should be directly under your wrists. Adult men should use a grip with 21 inches or 53 centimeters between their index fingers as a starting point. Women should use a grip four inches or ten centimeters narrower. Fine-tune from there to find the grip that gives you the proper forearm and elbow positioning. Once you find your optimum grip, have someone measure the distance between your index fingers, and make a written note of it.

Don't use a thumbless grip, because it reduces your control over the bar. Wrap your thumbs under and around the bar.

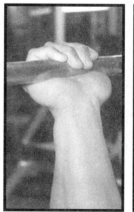
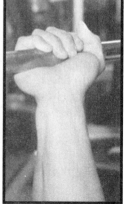

The thumbless or false grip on the left, and the correct grip on the right.

Grip with your hands equidistant from the bar's center. Be sure you're not even a fraction of an inch off center. Before a set, know precisely where your hands should be—use a tape measure if necessary.

If the back of your hands, wrists and forearms is in a straight line during the bench press, or any pressing movement, the bar will fall out of your hands. Your hands must move rearward sufficiently so that you can grip the bar securely. But don't allow the bar to extend your hands to the maximum, because that can mar your lifting technique, and injure your wrists. (The bar should be gripped firmly, because the slacker the grip, the less the actions of the flexors on the palm side of the forearm, which translates to less muscular counteraction to the rearward bending.) Once the bar is in a secure position in your hands, keep your wrists rigid for the duration of each set.

Performance

Get in position on the bench, hands in place on the bar, with a spotter or training partner standing directly behind you. Have the spotter or training partner give you a hand-off as you fully straighten and lock out your elbows. Pause until the bar is steady above your chest, inhale fully to fill your chest, pull your shoulders back, then immediately lower the bar under control. The full inhalation, and pulling back of the shoulders, help to produce the required tight, full torso. Take at least two to three seconds for the descent.

Lower the bar to a point below your nipples, at about the bottom line of your pectoral muscles. Find the precise point that's best for you. When the bar is on your chest, your forearms should be vertical when viewed from the side *and* the front (or rear, depending on where the viewer is). If they aren't, your hand spacing is incorrect.

Never bounce the bar off your chest. Touch your chest with the bar, pause there for one second, then push it up. Stay tight at the bottom with a full chest and firm grip—don't relax.

The ascent of the bar should be vertical, or slightly diagonal if that feels more natural—with just three or four inches of horizontal movement toward your head. Try both, and see which works best for you. Keep your forearms as vertical as possible during the ascent. Do this through keeping your elbows directly beneath your wrists. Exhale during the ascent.

Check yourself on a video recording, or have someone watch you from the side. What you may think, for example, is a vertical movement, may be angled slightly toward your feet. Practice until you can keep the bar moving correctly.

The ascent, just like the descent, should be symmetrical. The bar shouldn't tip to one side, both hands should move in unison, and you shouldn't take more weight on one side of your body than the other.

After locking out the bar, pause for a second or until the bar is stationary, inhale fully, pull your shoulders back, then again lower the bar slowly to the correct position on your lower chest.

The hand-off to start a bench press set (top), the top position prior to the descent of a rep (middle), and the bottom position at the lower pectoral line (above).

Common errors—DANGER

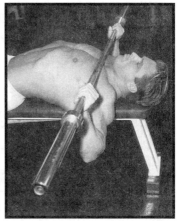

Two of the most common bench pressing errors. Left, exaggeration of the arch in the lower back—from having the feet behind the knees, and from not keeping the feet flat on the floor. NEVER DO THAT. *It has injured the lower backs of many trainees. Right, bench pressing to the upper chest.* NEVER DO THAT. *It has injured the shoulders of many trainees.*

Other tips

Keep your head flat on the bench. Never turn your head while you're lifting or lowering the bar. If you do, the bar may tip, and then your groove would be marred, and you could injure yourself.

Don't drive your head back into the bench, or otherwise you'll risk injury to your neck.

Use chalk or rosin on your hands to improve your grip on the bar, but keep the knurling clean.

When applying chalk, cover each hand, including the area on the inside of your thumb and index finger.

Once you've learned correct technique in the bench press, drill yourself on a fixed set-up and approach-to-the-bar procedure.

Once you've mastered bench pressing technique, give 100% attention to ensure that you deliver correct technique on every rep. Even a slight slip of concentration can lead to lowering the bar slightly out of position, or having one hand out of step with the other. Either of these will ruin your groove. This will make the weight feel heavier, make your reps harder, and risk injury.

Spotting

A hand-off to get the bar out of the saddles to start the set, is the first function of a spotter. During a set, as soon as the bar stalls or tips, or one hand gets forward of the other, the spotter must act to prevent the rep deteriorating further and causing injury.

The spotter must use both hands and provide sufficient assistance to keep the bar horizontal and moving correctly, centered above the lifter.

Even if the spotter doesn't need to assist during a rep, he should guide the bar back into the weight saddles after the final rep. At the end of a hard set of bench presses, you'll be tired. Without a guiding pair of hands on the bar from a spotter, you may miss getting the bar into the weight saddles. Throughout spotting, the spotter must not round his back, to protect *his* back.

How a single assistant should spot the bench press. This bench press unit has a platform for the spotter to stand on, for more efficient spotting.

Two pectoralis muscles

"Pectorals" and "pecs" refer to the pectoralis MAJOR—the large, flat muscle on each side of the upper rib cage. There's also the pectoralis MINOR, a much smaller muscle that's BENEATH the pectoralis major.

The pec minor protracts the scapula forward, as when a person reaches for something. The pec major is a prime mover of the humerus, as when a person bench presses, for example.

The pec minor isn't the upper pec, and doesn't make any significant contribution to chest development. What's considered to be the upper pec is the clavicular portion of the pectoralis major.

Technique recordings

Periodically, use a camcorder and record your exercise technique, for analysis later. A video camera can be an outstanding tool to help you to improve your exercise technique.

Dumbbell bench press

Main muscles worked

pectorals, deltoids, triceps

Capsule description

lie on your back, dumbbells in your hands, arms vertical, elbows locked; lower the dumbbells to your chest, then push them up

The bench press can also be done with dumbbells, again from a supine position on a horizontal bench. Once the 'bells are in pressing position, the technique is similar to the barbell version.

There are some advantages of the dumbbell version. First, provided there are suitable dumbbells available, you can probably dumbbell bench press whenever you want, and avoid having to wait your turn at the barbell bench press stations. Second, the dumbbell bench press doesn't require a power rack or other safety set-up, but a spotter is still required. Third, the 'bells provide more potential than a barbell does for optimizing hand and wrist positioning—a barbell fixes the hands into a pronated position.

The disadvantages of the dumbbell bench press are several. First, getting two heavy dumbbells into and out of position is difficult— and potentially dangerous—unless you have at least one competent assistant. Second, there's a greater chance of overstretching on the lowering phase than with a barbell. Third, balance is tricky, and if control is lost over one or both dumbbells during a set, you could sustain serious injury. In addition, the floor and equipment could be damaged if the dumbbells are dropped. Of course, the barbell bench press can be dangerous unless done correctly, inside a power rack with pins properly positioned.

Performance

To get into position for dumbbell bench pressing, have a spotter hand you the 'bells one at a time while you're in position on a bench (as you would be for the barbell bench press).

Alternatively, get the dumbbells into position by yourself. Sit on the end of a bench with the 'bells held vertically on your thighs. Center your hands on the handles. Keep your elbows bent, chin on your chest, *back rounded*, and, with a thrust on the 'bells from your thighs, *roll* back on the bench and position your feet properly, like for the barbell bench press. With your forearms vertical, and hands lined up with your lower pecs, inhale fully to fill your chest, pull your shoulders back, and immediately begin pressing.

Press in a similar pathway as in the barbell version. Keep the 'bells moving in tandem, as if they were linked. Don't let them drift outward from your torso, or let one get ahead of the other.

Clockwise, from the bottom left, how to get into position, without assistance, for the dumbbell bench press, and the first ascent of the set.

With dumbbells you don't have to hold your hands as if holding a barbell. Use a parallel grip, or one somewhere in between that and the barbell-style pronated grip. You can change your wrist positioning during the course of each rep.

If the back of your hands, wrists and forearms is in a straight line during the dumbbell bench press, or *any* pressing movement, the dumbbells will fall out of your hands. Your hands must extend rearward sufficiently so that you can grip the dumbbells securely. But don't allow the dumbbells to extend your hands to the maximum, because that can mar your lifting technique, and injure your wrists. (The dumbbells should be gripped firmly, because the slacker the grip, the less the actions of the flexors on the palm side of the forearm, which translates to less of a muscular counteraction to the rearward bending.) Once the dumbbells are in a secure position in your hands, keep your wrists rigid for the duration of each set.

Don't seek an exaggerated range of motion. Keep your hands near to the spacing that was recommended for the barbell bench press. Don't use a wider grip so that you can get your hands lower at the bottom of the exercise. Descend to a point no deeper than you would on a barbell bench press. Pause at the bottom for a second, then ascend smoothly, under control. Pause for a second at the top, or until the dumbbells are stationary, then smoothly perform the next rep.

From the top, the last descent of a set of dumbbell bench presses, and the return to the seated position.

Your control may be poor at first, but with practice you'll develop control over the dumbbells.

Adding weight

Fixed-weight dumbbells usually increase in increments of 5 pounds (or 2.5 kilos). Going up in dumbbells usually means a total increase of 10 pounds, which is large. Stick with a pair of dumbbells until you can comfortably do several reps more than your target count, before going up in weight the next time you dumbbell bench press.

If you use adjustable dumbbells, you can use smaller increments than 5 pounds provided you have small discs. Even if you use fixed-weight dumbbells, you can attach two small discs to each dumbbell. Use strong adhesive tape and ensure that the discs are securely attached. Over time, build up to the weight of the next pair of fixed-weight dumbbells. To ensure proper balance, attach the small discs in pairs to each dumbbell, one at each end. A better choice is to use magnetic small plates.

Spotting

A spotter should crouch behind your head, ready to provide assistance. One hand should apply force under each elbow. But this is strictly for assisting a lifter to get a tough rep up in correct technique. A single person can't simultaneously take a pair of 'bells from someone who fails on a rep. Two spotters are needed, then.

Don't push this exercise to failure. Even when you're training hard, stop this exercise one rep short of failure, so you don't risk losing control. Losing control could cost you an injury. Even an alert spotter may not be able to prevent loss of control of both dumbbells.

A spotter, or better still two spotters, can take the dumbbells off you at the end of a set. Alternatively, get off the bench while holding the dumbbells. Here's how, as illustrated on the left: Lower the 'bells to your lower torso, keep your forearms, arms, shoulders and chest tight, and lift your bent knees as high as you can. With the 'bells touching your thighs, and your chin on your chest, immediately throw your feet forward and roll into a seated position. This is especially easy to do if a spotter places his hands under your shoulders and helps you to roll up.

A spotter should be careful not to round his back while spotting you, to protect *his* back.

Close-grip bench press

Main muscles worked

triceps, pectorals, deltoids

Capsule description

lie on your back, bar in your hands with a shoulder-width grip, arms vertical, elbows locked; lower the bar to your chest, then push it up

This exercise is similar to the standard barbell bench press. The principal difference is the grip spacing. The closer grip increases the involvement of the triceps. The section on the barbell bench press should be studied together with this one.

Set-up and positioning

The commonly seen close-grip bench press has the hands touching, or very close together. This is harmful for the wrists, and the elbows. The safe close-grip bench press is not very close. Make it about five inches or 13 centimeters closer than your regular-grip bench press. Depending on torso girth, and forearm and arm lengths, about 16 inches or 41 centimeters between index fingers will probably be fine for most men, and about 12 inches or 30 centimeters for women. Find what feels most comfortable for you. If in doubt, go wider rather than narrower. Apply the bench press rule of keeping your forearms vertical—vertical as seen from the front *and* from the sides.

Position yourself on the bench like in the standard bench press, and don't use a thumbless grip.

Performance

Take your grip on the bar and get a hand-off to help you to get the bar out of the saddles. Keep your elbows straight, move the bar into the starting position above your lower chest, and pause briefly. Inhale fully and fill your chest, pull your shoulders back, keep a tight torso, and start the descent. Bring your elbows in a little as you lower the bar, to keep your elbows beneath your wrists.

The bar should touch your chest at the line of your lower pecs, or a little lower. Never bounce the bar off your chest. Touch your chest and pause there for one second, then push the bar up. Stay tight at the bottom, with a full chest and firm grip—don't relax. Exhale during the ascent.

The hand spacing of the standard bench press (left) and a safe close-grip bench press (right). In this case the difference is only about five inches or 13 centimeters. The bar is at the lower pectoral line in both cases. The elbows should be directly beneath the wrists. In the illustration on the right, the hands could be brought in a little further provided the elbows follow. A shoulder-width grip is ideal.

The ascent of the bar should be vertical, or *slightly* diagonal if that feels more natural—with just a few inches of horizontal movement toward your head. Try both, and see which works best for you.

During the ascent of the bar it may be natural for your elbows to move outward a little, prior to their return to a line directly beneath your wrists as you near the top position. This especially applies if there's any horizontal movement during the ascent.

Hand positioning this close is dangerous, especially for the wrists and elbows.

Other tips

The narrowed grip relative to the standard bench press can cause excessive extension of the shoulders, especially in long-limbed, lanky trainees. If the close-grip bench press bothers your shoulders, and you're doing the exercise as described here, modify the movement.

Do the exercise in a power rack with pins set so that you reduce the range of motion by a few inches. That will reduce the extension of your shoulders, and make the exercise safer.

Fatigue occurs suddenly in the close-grip bench press. Use a set-up that will safely catch the bar if you have to dump it—see the set-up guidelines for the standard barbell bench press. Terminate a set as soon as your elbows start to drift out of position despite your best efforts to keep them in position.

Spotting

See the guidelines for the standard barbell bench press. Similar guidelines for spotting apply here. But because fatigue occurs more suddenly in the close-grip bench press, your spotter must be especially alert. He must be ready to help you when the bar stalls, or when your elbows start to drift out of position.

Even if exercise technique is correct, rep speed is controlled, and the handling of weights is faultless while setting up equipment, an exercise can still cause problems if, for a given individual, training is excessive in terms of frequency or volume, or if the adding of weight to the bar is rushed.

Incline barbell bench press

Main muscles worked

pectorals, deltoids, triceps

the incline bench press may place more stress on the upper pectorals (clavicular head) than does the horizontal, supine version

Capsule description

lie on your back on an incline bench, bar overhead; lower bar to your chest, then push it up

Set-up

Use a heavy-duty, adjustable bench, preferably one that has an adjustment for tilting the seat—to prevent the user slipping out of position. Use a low-incline bench that has an angle no greater than 30 degrees with the horizontal. Most incline benches are set too upright for this exercise.

Ideally, do the exercise in a power rack, with pins properly positioned for safety. Alternatively, do the exercise in a purpose-built, incline bench press unit. If you do the exercise outside the safety of a power rack, have a spotter standing by in case you get stuck on a rep. The spotter is also needed to help you to get the bar out of the saddles safely, and return it to the saddles after the set is over.

An incline bench press unit, with built-in (black) adjustable safety bars. An unloaded barbell is shown resting across the unit's bar saddles.

Grip, and bar placement

Start with the same grip as in the standard bench press, and fine-tune if necessary. Don't use a thumbless grip, but wrap your thumbs around the bar properly. Furthermore, as in the bench press, your hands must extend rearward sufficiently so that you can grip the bar securely. But don't allow the bar to extend your hands to the maximum, because that can mar your lifting technique, and injure your wrists. Grip the bar firmly, to help keep your wrists in the right position. Once the bar is in a secure position in your hands, keep your wrists rigid for the duration of each set.

Don't lower the bar as low on your chest as in the regular bench press. Because of the inclination of the bench, a low position of the bar on your chest would lead to excessive and unsafe extension of your shoulders. Nor should you lower the bar to your neck or clavicles— that positioning is also dangerous for your shoulders.

Rather than wonder where to place the bar on your chest at the bottom of the incline press, look at it in terms of your forearms and arms. Your forearms should be vertical at the bottom—vertical when viewed from the side *and* from the front. (Get the help of an assistant.) At that position your

Top, hand spacing a little too wide. Bottom, better hand spacing, elbows directly beneath the wrists.

arms should be at about a 45 to 60 degree angle to your rib cage. The precise angle will vary from individual to individual, largely because of forearm and arm lengths, and torso girth variations. Get your forearms in the right position, and you should automatically find the ideal placement of the bar on your chest.

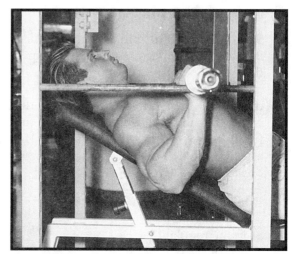

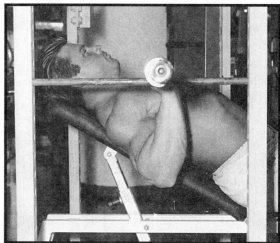

Your forearms should be vertical when viewed from the side. Top photograph, bar too low on the chest, which produces excessive shoulder extension. Above, correct positioning.

Performance

Position yourself on the incline bench, and plant your feet solidly on the floor, or on a foot brace if one is provided. Keep your feet fixed in position. Don't lift or shuffle them. Your feet should be flat on the floor, wider than shoulder width. Feet positioned close together reduce stability.

With a hand-off, take the barbell out of the stands. Straighten your elbows, pause for a second, then lower the bar under control. Touch your chest at the position explained earlier, and pause for a second. Keep yourself tight during the pause, with your abdominal muscles, buttocks, and lats contracted. Then smoothly press up and slightly back. After straightening your elbows, pause for a second, or until the bar is stationary, then lower it for the next rep.

Use the same breathing pattern as in the regular bench press.

Spotting

See *Bench press*. The same guidelines apply to spotting the incline barbell press. In addition, the spotter needs to be elevated, to apply assistance with least difficulty. For the spotter to avoid injury, he must maintain a slightly hollowed lower back, and get as close to the trainee as possible.

Caution

When you incline press, don't exaggerate the hollow in your lower back. With your feet flat on the floor, keep your heels directly beneath or slightly in front of an imaginary vertical line drawn through the middle of your knees. If your feet are behind your knees, the arch will probably be exaggerated, and the risk of injury increased.

But, if the seat of the bench is too high and can't be adjusted, or if you have short lower limbs, this strategy won't work well. A non-slip, low block or platform under each foot will be required. A wide single platform would also do the job. The wider your feet, the greater your stability.

When preparing to unrack the bar from behind your head to get ready for the first rep of a set of the incline barbell bench press, don't draw your elbows behind your wrists, or even in line with your wrists. If your elbows are drawn back, then as you unrack the bar the stress on your shoulders will be increased greatly, and unnecessarily. Keep your elbows in front of your wrists while you unrack the bar. But provided you use a spotter, you won't have to take much of the strain from unracking the bar while getting set up for the first rep.

Incline dumbbell bench press

Main muscles worked

pectorals, deltoids, triceps

the incline bench press may place more stress on the upper pectorals (clavicular head) than does the horizontal, supine version

Capsule description

lie on your back on an incline bench, with the dumbbells overhead; lower the dumbbells to your chest, then push them up

The incline bench press can also be done with dumbbells. Once the dumbbells are in position for pressing, the technique is basically the same as in the barbell version.

A big advantage of dumbbells is that you can use whatever wrist positioning is most comfortable, rather than have your wrists fixed by a barbell into a pronated position. But there are handling difficulties getting the 'bells into position. See *Dumbbell bench press* for the main pros and cons of dumbbell bench pressing.

As in other pressing movements, your hands must extend rearward sufficiently so that you can grip the dumbbells securely. But don't allow the dumbbells to extend your hands to the maximum, because that can mar your lifting technique, and injure your wrists. Grip the bar firmly, to help keep your wrists in the right position. Once the dumbbells are in a secure position in your hands, keep your wrists rigid for the duration of each set.

To perform the dumbbell incline bench press, you require a method for getting the dumbbells into position ready for pressing. See *Dumbbell bench press* for how to do this.

During the pressing, pay special attention to keeping the dumbbells from drifting out to the sides, go no deeper than in the barbell version, and keep the 'bells moving in tandem. You'll probably need a few workouts to get the feel for the exercise, and to find the wrist positioning that best suits you.

See *Dumbbell bench press* for tips on how to progress gradually from one pair of fixed-weight dumbbells, to the next.

Spotting

See *Dumbbell bench press*. The same guidelines apply to spotting the incline dumbbell bench press, but in the latter there's no need for the spotter to crouch.

With any type of dumbbell pressing, key markers of technique deterioration are the 'bells drifting out to the sides, and one hand getting above, in front of, or to the rear of the other. Don't push this exercise to failure. Stop a rep short of failure, so that you don't risk losing control of the 'bells.

Caution

Don't exaggerate the hollow in your lower back. See *Incline barbell bench press*.

3. CALF RAISE

Main muscles worked

gastrocnemius, soleus

Capsule description

stand with the balls of your feet fixed, then raise and lower your heels

The soleus is underneath the gastrocnemius, so most of the soleus isn't visible, but it still contributes significantly to calf girth. The soleus crosses the ankle joint only, but the gastrocnemius crosses the ankle *and* knee joints. Both muscles plantar flex the foot—namely, point the toes—but the gastrocnemius also assists with flexion of the knee.

The calf raise is often called a *heel raise*. Confusingly, it's also sometimes called a *toe raise* even though the toes don't rise.

There are several types of calf raises: standing using both legs, standing using one leg at a time, seated (usually with both legs working simultaneously), and donkey style (where an assistant sits on the bent-over trainee's hips, for added resistance). Avoid the leg press machine for calf work. This offers nothing that other calf exercises don't, but can be dangerous if your feet slip out of position.

Keeping your knees straight in calf work, or just slightly bent, fully recruits the gastrocnemius *and* the soleus. Bent-knee calf work—especially the seated calf raise—reduces gastrocnemius involvement according to the extent of knee flexion.

The standing two-legged calf raise, and the one-legged variation, are the calf exercises used in the routines in this book. Both of these exercises fully involve the gastrocnemius and soleus simultaneously.

Set-up and positioning

In all calf work, place the balls of your feet on a stable block, to enable your heels to descend below the level of the balls of your feet. If the block is free standing—not attached to a calf machine—fix it to a board that has a larger area. This will prevent the block from flipping over. For example, get a 4 x 4 x 20 inch piece of wood and nail it to the center of a 1 x 10 x 22 inch board. Round one of the top two long edges of the block, for the side where you'll place your feet. As an alternative, at least for the dumbbell one-legged calf raise, use an immovable object such as a step.

Depending on the soles of your shoes and the surface you stand on, your feet may slip out of position during the course of a set of calf raises. If this happens, quickly reposition your feet, but next time try different shoes or a different platform or block (perhaps one with rubber fixed on top of it) to help prevent your feet from slipping. Slipping can, however, be caused by incorrect foot positioning, and excessive range of motion at the bottom of the exercise.

If the full range of motion produces foot problems, cut your range of motion a little. Find the maximum range of motion that's safe for you, and which doesn't lead to your feet slipping off the elevation.

Your calves may be tight at present. The calf stretch described in this book should help you to increase the flexibility of your calves. Then as your flexibility improves you may be able to increase your depth of descent in the calf raise.

As well as the aesthetic benefits of calf development, there are health benefits from regular calf exercise. With age, the return of blood to the heart through the veins decreases in efficiency. This is prominent below the knees, and may lead to varicose veins because of blood pooling, and damage to the venous valves. The venous blood is moved upward through muscle contraction. Inactivity of the calves increases the difficulty of getting the venous blood to the heart. Keep your calves strong and trained.

Standing two-legged calf raise

A machine is needed for this exercise. If one isn't available, stick with the one-legged calf raise.

Compression of the spine may occur in the standing two-legged calf raise *if* your heels touch the floor *before* the resistance reaches its resting position. Set up the machine so that the resistance rests on a support *before* your heels touch the floor. Alternatively, use a block high enough so that it's impossible to touch your heels to the floor even at full stretch. If you can't ensure you don't risk compressing your spine, change to the dumbbell one-legged calf raise.

When you get positioned for the first rep of any machine standing calf raise, distribute the weight symmetrically over your back and lower limbs, but don't round your upper back. Put the pads in position on your shoulders, pull your shoulder blades back, bend your knees, and place your feet in position on the foot support. Put the entire balls of your feet on the support, not just your toes. Use a hip-width foot placement rather than a close stance, to help you to keep your balance. Keep your big toes pointing directly forward or slightly outward. None of the stress of the weight should be taken on your shoulders yet. Now, hollow your lower back slightly, lock your torso, and straighten your knees. Then you'll safely be in the starting position for the first rep, with the resistance bearing down on you.

Don't take the full load of the resistance on your shoulders and then shuffle into position on the foot support or block. Get correctly in position *before* you take on the resistance.

Hold the calf machine during the exercise, to help keep your balance and maintain a rigid torso. During the course of each set, never allow your back to round, torso to relax, or knees to bend anything more than just slightly, to remove tension from your knees.

Perform your reps smoothly. Go as high as possible at the top of each rep, and contract your calves hard for two to three seconds. Descend under control, reach your safe, bottom position, pause for a second without relaxing, then smoothly push out of it. Never bounce at the bottom of a rep.

Left, correct technique for the standing calf raise—note the proper curvature of the spine. Right, don't round your back while performing any machine standing calf raise.

Some squat machines, with the addition of a block under the balls of the feet, can double as calf machines. Keep your knees straight or just slightly bent.

Standing one-legged calf raise

The one-legged calf raise is done while holding a dumbbell on the same side as your working calf, using a standing calf machine, or with resistance hanging from a belt. With a dumbbell, hold with your free hand something sturdy and stable at about shoulder height, to keep your balance—for example, a bar set at the right height in a power rack.

Put the entire ball of your foot on the elevation, not just your toes. Keep the knee of your working leg straight or just slightly bent during each set, and your big toe pointing directly forward or slightly outward. Bend your non-working limb and keep it out of the way— for example, rest it on the heel of your working limb.

Perform your reps smoothly. Go as high as possible at the top of each rep, and contract your calves hard for two to three seconds. Descend under control, reach your safe, bottom position, pause for a second without relaxing, then smoothly push out of it. Never bounce at the bottom of a rep.

Left, one-legged dumbbell calf raise, holding a horizontal bar for balance. Right, one-legged calf raise using a calf machine.

In all calf work, avoid an exaggerated range of motion at the bottom of the exercise. If you overstretch, you'll lose your foot positioning, and have to re-set, which would mar the set. Descend as far as is comfortable for you without it leading to your feet slipping. Calf stretching should be done during a flexibility routine, not while strength training.

4. CHIN-UP (AND PULL-UP)

Main muscles worked

latissimus dorsi, biceps, brachialis, pectorals, upper back, abdominal wall, forearms

Capsule description

holding a fixed overhead bar, pull yourself up to the bar

There's confusion with the names *chin-up* and *pull-up*. In this book, the chin-up refers to pulling yourself up on an overhead bar using a supinated grip, and the pull-up refers to the same movement but with a pronated grip. Many trainees, however, use the two names interchangeably, regardless of the grip used.

Your ability to pull yourself overhead is influenced by your bodyfat percentage, and your bodyweight in general. The more bodyfat you have, and the heavier you are, the harder this exercise will be.

Set-up and positioning

If your overhead bar is adjustable—for example, if you use an Olympic bar on saddles in a power rack—set the height so you can just grab the bar when standing on your toes. The knurling on an Olympic bar will help your grip, especially if you have chalk or rosin on your hands.

If you use a fixed, high, overhead bar, arrange a box or platform of the appropriate height so that you only have to stand on your toes to grab the bar. During the exercise, bend your knees, or keep them straight.

Initially, hold the overhead bar with a supinated grip. Start with a shoulder-width grip, and fine-tune to find the spacing that feels best for your wrists and elbows. A hand spacing a little closer than shoulder-width may work best.

If you can't find a workable supinated grip, try a pronated one. Take a pronated grip that's two to three inches wider on each side than your shoulder-width grip, so that your forearms are vertical at the contracted position. Regardless of the grip you choose, never use a very wide spacing, and don't pull to the rear of your head. Pulling to the front is safer for your shoulders and neck, and more effective.

A Smith machine has a bar that's adjustable for height, and may be well-knurled. It may be ideal for chin-ups and pull-ups.

Some chinning units provide the option of using a parallel grip. This may be more comfortable than a supinated or a pronated grip on a single bar. The parallel handles may, however, be too close to produce a good training effect.

A possibility for chinning with a parallel grip is to use a power rack. If its uprights are appropriately spaced for you, position a bar on saddles on the front uprights, and another bar across the rear uprights at the same height. Set the height of the bars so that when your elbows are straight, your feet *just* touch the floor.

Performance

Pull until you touch the bar to your collar bones, or lower on your chest. Comparing the same resistance and degree of effort, you'll be able to pull your hands to a lower point on your chest with a supinated or pronated grip than with a parallel one. Fully contract your lats by pulling your shoulder blades *down*.

Top, chin-up (supinated grip). Above, pull-up (pronated grip).

Your top position will depend, in part, on your grip spacing, forearm and arm lengths, and your strength and bodyweight. Don't pull beyond what's comfortable for your shoulders and elbows. Your back should be slightly arched at the top of the exercise. If you have to hump your back in order to finish a rep, the set is finished, you're using too much resistance, or you're not ready, yet, for this exercise.

Pause for a second at the top position, then smoothly lower yourself to an inch short of the bottommost position. Pause for a second at the bottom, then smoothly move into the next ascent. Never drop into the bottom position, or relax and stretch while you're hanging. Keep your eyes looking up slightly, and don't turn your head. Keep your shoulders tight, and your head tilted back, but don't throw your head back.

Inhale as you lower yourself, and exhale during the ascent. Trying to catch your breath during a momentary pause at the bottom position is usually counterproductive unless you can briefly stand or kneel while you breathe.

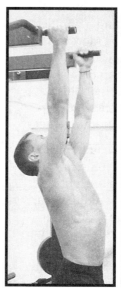

Use of a parallel grip.

Other tips

Attach weight securely and comfortably. Use a shoulder harness or a belt designed for hanging weight from, wear a belt and put a dumbbell inside it by having the dumbbell vertical and the belt across the handle, or, use a strong piece of rope or chain to attach a dumbbell or weight plates securely to a belt. For the latter, the resistance can be hung from the front or the rear of the belt. Try both to find which is most comfortable for you.

Add weight slowly, in small increments. To work from one fixed-weight dumbbell to the next, gradually attach weight to the lighter dumbbell—most easily done by using small magnetic plates. Alternatively, use an adjustable dumbbell, or weight plates only.

Spotting

Though not essential, use a spotter if possible. When you grind to a halt short of completing a rep, get a spotter to assist. Enough pressure should be evenly applied to your back. The assistant should push you up in your regular groove, not push you forward and mar the pathway.

Three methods of attaching weight to a belt. These illustrations show use of a lifting belt. Use of a purpose-made weight belt would be better. And at least for small weights, a strong, leather belt normally used for trousers could substitute.

A shoulder harness isn't illustrated, but is the preferred option—for safety, and comfort—if a substantial poundage is to be attached to a suspended body. A substantial poundage attached around the waist or hips may apply an unsafe load on the spine during the chin-up and pull-up because the body is suspended and the forces pulling on the vertebrae may be excessive.

The free-weight parallel bar dip—another exercise where the body is suspended—has a greater potential for additional weight to be attached than have the chin-up and pull-up. But a very strong person may build up to a large weight in the latter two exercises and thus should use a shoulder harness rather than a weight belt.

5. CRUNCH

Five forms of the crunch will be described:
    basic crunch
    modified basic crunch
    machine crunch
    reverse crunch
    twisting crunch

Main muscles worked

rectus abdominis, external and internal abdominal obliques, transversus abdominis, hip flexors, (and the twisting crunch also works the multifidii)

Capsule description

curl your shoulders toward your hips, or your hips toward your shoulders

Exercise for the abdominal muscles is important, and not just for aesthetic reasons. Strong, well-developed abdominals help to keep the lower back strong and resistant to injury because they help to stabilize the spine during many exercises.

Crunches come in two basic types: The basic crunch curls the shoulders toward the hips, and the reverse crunch curls the hips toward the chest. Each works both functions of the rectus abdominis and transversus abdominis—compression of the abdomen, and flexion of the trunk—but only two of the functions of the obliques: compression of the abdomen, and flexion of the trunk. A third function of the obliques—trunk rotation—isn't worked by most crunches. The *twisting* crunch employs rotation.

The rectus abdominis ("six-pack") is one long, flat, continuous muscle that runs from the lower ribs to the groin. While it's not possible to isolate the upper or lower abdominals, the two sections may respond differently to flexion exercises that require the shoulders to move toward the hips, than to flexion exercises that require the hips to move toward the shoulders.

Trainees commonly get poor results from crunches for two main reasons: many perform excessive reps with little or no added resistance, and most use incorrect technique regardless of their rep count. With correct technique, moderate reps, and progressive resistance, good results will come. *But whether you'll see your abdominal development will depend on how much fat you have covering your midsection.*

Preparatory movement

Before every rep of any crunch, tilt your hips so that your lumbar vertebrae are pushed into the floor or mat.

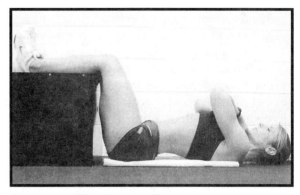

Basic crunch

Lie on a mat next to a bench. Bend your knees at a right angle and rest your calves on the bench. Don't cross your legs. Get an assistant to hold your legs on the bench, use a purpose-built bench with a leg restraint, or brace your feet in some way so that your legs stay fixed to the bench. Cross your hands and rest them on your chest or shoulders. Before each rep, tilt your pelvis so that while your coccyx and sacrum come off the floor a little (that is, your buttocks rise slightly), your lumbar vertebrae are pushed into the floor. Smoothly curl your torso off the floor until your forearms touch your thighs. Pause for a second at the top position, and contract your abdominals hard. Then take about three seconds to smoothly unfurl onto the floor. Maintain the pelvic tilt during the ascent and descent. Once your shoulders are on

the floor, pause for a second, again push your lumbar vertebrae into the floor (that is, tilt your pelvis), and repeat.

Don't hold your breath. Exhale fully before the concentric or lifting phase, and inhale during the descent.

Keep your head and neck in one fixed position throughout each rep, with your chin slightly off your chest.

A common mistake is putting the hands behind the head. This leads to pulling on the head, causing neck irritation. When you require resistance, hold a dumbbell across your chest, with the handle parallel with your shoulders. You could hold small plates on your chest, but large plates will obstruct the proper movement. Once you've progressed beyond using small plates, move to a dumbbell. Be consistent with where you place the dumbbell on your mid to upper chest, so that you apply resistance in the same way each time. If you vary the position of the dumbbell, you'll change the perceived weight of the resistance.

Loading and unloading the resistance can be a problem—because asymmetrical movement is involved in taking a dumbbell from the floor at one side, for example. Have an assistant put the dumbbell directly on your chest, and remove it for you at the end of the set.

The basic crunch with a dumbbell held horizontally on the chest.

Hip flexors, and abdominal work

The hip flexors are involved in most forms of abdominal work, including crunches. (The iliopsoas hip flexors—iliacus, psoas major, and psoas minor—are located deep in the pelvis, and are hidden from view. The other major hip flexor, the rectus femoris, is visible—it's part of the quadriceps.) The degree of involvement of the hip flexors depends on the technique used. Abdominal work with straight knees may employ the hip flexors to a greater extent than the abs, and should be avoided. By keeping the knees bent, the involvement of the hip flexors is reduced, and the relative involvement of the abs is increased. Substantial hip flexor involvement can produce lower-back problems for many trainees— typically those whose lower backs aren't strong enough, and who lack sufficient flexibility. Generally, the greater the hip flexor involvement in abdominal work, the greater the possibility of lower-back irritation.

If you've had any back problems, use the *modified* basic crunch for a few months before you consider progressing to the full-range basic crunch. The modified crunch has a reduced range of motion relative to the basic crunch, and involves the hip flexors to a lesser extent. This reduced hip flexor involvement means reduced stress on the lower back. In the meantime, get checked out by a chiropractor, strengthen your abs with the modified basic crunch, strengthen your lower back with back extensions, and work on the flexibility routine.

The hip flexor involvement in the basic crunch is desirable *provided* the exercise can be done safely. The hip flexors need to be strengthened, too, once the lower back and abs have been sufficiently strengthened. What's required is balanced strength across the three areas.

Modified basic crunch

Adopt the same set-up as for the basic crunch, although it may not be necessary to have your calves held against the bench. The modified crunch is a short-range exercise. Only about half your spine should come off the floor. Your lumbar vertebrae must retain contact with the floor throughout each rep.

Use a slow ascent and forcible crunch of your abdominal muscles. Hold the top position for a second. Slowly lower your upper back to the floor. Move smoothly at all times.

Don't hold your breath. Exhale fully before the concentric or lifting phase, and inhale during the descent.

Why sit-ups with straight knees are dangerous

Especially in days gone by, school students and youngsters elsewhere were urged by instructors to perform quick-fire sit-ups with their knees straight, and hands interlocked behind their heads or necks. That technique can be harmful even for youngsters, and is potentially harmful for most adults. Avoid it.

Crunches are safe, relative to sit-ups, because the knees are bent, the hips are flexed, and the lower back is rounded to the *rear*. As a result, the abdominal muscles pull you up and forward, and the hip flexors help

Machine crunch

Follow the manufacturer's guidelines for the set-up.

Smoothly flex the upper half of your spine. Crunch your torso forward, hold the intense contraction for a second, then smoothly return to the starting position. Pause for a second, then smoothly begin the next rep.

Don't hold your breath. Exhale fully before the flexion phase, and inhale during the extension.

Compare the effect from the machine on your abdominals with that from the non-machine crunches. The latter may be better, because many crunch machines aren't well designed.

The crunch machine shown on the left has the resistance arms above the chest. The other one has a resistance pad applied against the chest.

as synergists (not prime movers) to keep the pelvis stabilized at the crucial moment the crunch is initiated by the rectus abdominis muscles.

But in sit-ups with straight knees, the hip flexors are the prime movers as they first pull the lower back into a more arched position (curved to the *front*), and *then* they pull the torso up and forward. It's this initial pull on the lumbar arch that feels uncomfortable, and commonly creates problems.

Perform crunches, not sit-ups with straight knees.

Reverse crunch

Lie on your back on a horizontal bench. Hold the bench behind your head. With straight knees, lift your legs so that they are perpendicular to the bench. Keep your feet directly above your hips, and bend your knees so that they are above your lower chest. Tilt your pelvis so that while your coccyx and sacrum come off the floor a little, your lumbar vertebrae are pushed into the bench. Initiate every rep in this manner. Then roll your lower back off the bench. Hold the top position for a second, then slowly return to the starting position. Pause for a second, tilt your pelvis again, and smoothly move into the next rep.

This is a short-range movement. Maintain the pelvic tilt throughout each rep. At no point should you arch or hollow your lower back.

Don't hold your breath. Exhale fully before the concentric or lifting phase, and inhale during the descent.

Performing the reverse crunch on a horizontal bench with your feet above your hips and knees bent above your lower chest, provides low resistance. To increase the resistance, straighten your knees but keep your feet above your hips. To further increase the resistance, keep your thighs perpendicular to the bench, and knees bent so that your feet are in front of your hips. Progress until you can perform your target reps with your knees bent at a right angle and thighs vertical. For increased resistance thereafter, perform the reverse crunch on an incline bench, with your head higher than your hips in the starting position.

Remember to tilt your pelvis so that your lower back (other than your coccyx and sacrum) is flattened against the bench prior to each rep—for safety, and to focus the stress on your abdominal muscles.

In all variations of the reverse crunch, don't jam your head onto the bench, because that could cause neck injury. Maintain a relaxed neck, and keep the strain of the exercise on your abdominals.

The topmost photographs show the least demanding of these three forms of the reverse crunch. If required, the resistance can be further reduced by bringing the knees closer to the chest.

The bottommost photographs show the most demanding of these three forms of the reverse crunch. To make it even more taxing, perform the reverse crunch on an inclined bench, with your head above your hips in the starting position—the photograph on the left page shows the top position. Start with little inclination, and increase the degree of slope gradually.

Twisting crunch

This crunch variation increases the involvement of both obliques, because it involves rotation of the trunk. The rest of the abdominal wall is involved, too. *Because it involves rotation of the trunk, this crunch also works the multifidii.* This muscle group is deep to the erector spinae, from the sacrum to the neck, and extends and rotates the vertebral column.

Adopt the same set-up for the basic crunch, and perform the movement in the same way except add a slight twist during the ascent. As you ascend—following a hip tilt, and full exhalation—point your left elbow toward your right inner thigh. Hold the top, slightly twisted position for a second, then as you descend, return to the symmetrical position. On the next rep, point your right elbow toward your left inner thigh, and so on. Just a slight twist is enough to increase greatly the involvement of the obliques. Although there's asymmetry in this exercise, it's safe, and necessary.

When you twist to your right, you use your right external oblique, and your *left* internal oblique. When you twist to your left, you use your left external oblique, and your *right* internal oblique.

A purpose-built bench with leg restraints, suitable for the basic crunch (illustrated), modified crunch, and twisting crunch.

Prior to each rep of any form of the crunch, remember to tilt your pelvis so that your lower back (other than your coccyx and sacrum) is flattened against the bench, floor, or mat—for safety, and to focus the stress on your abdominal muscles.

6. CURL

Main muscles worked

biceps, brachialis, brachioradialis, forearms

Capsule description

standing or seated, arms and forearms hanging straight, lift the weight through bending at your elbows

The curl can be done with dumbbells or a barbell, standing or seated. If done seated, use dumbbells in order to extend your forearms fully. There are also cable and machine variations of the curl.

The biceps flex the elbows *and* supinate the hands. To supinate your hands fully, rotate them from a palms-down to a palms-up position. You can't do this with a barbell. The biceps isn't the only elbow flexor. There are the brachialis (beneath the biceps) and the brachioradialis (from just above the elbow, to the wrist), too, which are also worked by the curl. The latter two muscles flex the elbow only, they don't supinate the hand.

While permitting supination and a full range of motion even while seated, the dumbbell curl produces another advantage over the barbell curl—the ability for the wrists and elbows to adopt the most comfortable positioning.

In all curls, keep your wrists and hands in a straight line—the neutral position. If you don't maintain the neutral position, you may develop wrist and elbow problems.

Spotting

Technique deterioration is shown through leaning back (unless you use back support) and bringing the elbows too far forward. As soon as your torso goes back even a whisker beyond the vertical, your spotter should urge you to straighten up. If you perform another rep, a little assistance may be needed if you're to complete the rep in correct technique. Assistance should be applied with two hands, in a symmetrical way. Just enough help should be given to keep your torso and arms vertical.

The correct, straight, or neutral position of hands and wrists (top), and the incorrect position (above).

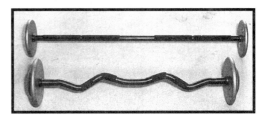

Comparison of a straight bar and an EZ-curl bar. The EZ-curl bar may be more comfortable to use for the barbell curl than a straight bar.

Seated dumbbell curl

Sit at the end of a bench, with your knees together, and feet on the floor. Hold a dumbbell in each hand, with straight elbows, hands parallel with each other, an upright torso, and your shoulders retracted.

Curl the dumbbells, don't swing them—move smoothly. As the dumbbells ascend, supinate your hands as much as possible—rotate your thumbs outward. On the descent, pronate your hands so that, in the starting position, they are parallel with each other once again.

Start with your elbows at your sides so that your arms are vertical when viewed from the side and from the front. As you curl, your elbows may come forward only *slightly*. At the top position, your hands should be several inches short of where they would be to make your forearms vertical. Your hands may come to shoulder height, but no higher.

Pause for a second in the top position. Contract your biceps hard at the top position as you fully supinate your wrists. It's not possible to rest at the top of a properly performed curl. Lower the resistance under control, pause for a second at the bottom position, then smoothly perform the next rep. Exhale during the ascent, and inhale during the descent.

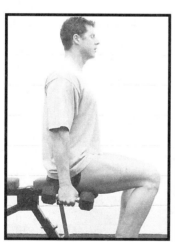

Incline dumbbell curl

Perform the dumbbell curl with your hips, back, and shoulders against an incline bench set at about 45 degrees. For comfort, your head doesn't have to rest against the bench. To make it easy to pick up the dumbbells from the floor, use the lowest seat setting, if it's adjustable. And because of the incline bench, your arms may not be perfectly vertical. Otherwise, the technique is the same as for the *Seated dumbbell curl*.

Barbell curl

Stand with your feet about hip-width apart. Keep your knees slightly unlocked, and your buttocks tensed, to help support your spine. Use a supinated (palms-up) grip on the barbell, with hands spaced a little wider than hip-width. Fine-tune this to find the hand spacing that's most comfortable for your wrists and elbows. Other than there being no wrist rotation in the barbell curl, the rest of the technique is the same as for the *Seated dumbbell curl.*

If the straight bar irritates your elbows or wrists, try a closer or wider grip. If that doesn't correct the problem, try the EZ-curl bar. If that doesn't produce a comfortable curl, use dumbbells. An EZ-curl bar is a short barbell that has a number of bends or cambers in it, to enable the user to try to find the grip that feels the most comfortable.

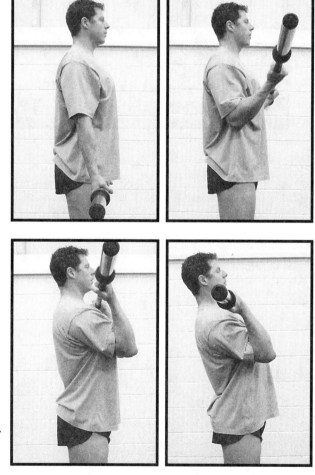

Correct starting and finishing positions (above). Incorrect finishing positions (right).

Hammer curl

Different wrist positions produce different effects on the elbow flexors, and apply stress differently to the elbow joints. One alternative is to keep your thumbs *up* all the time—the *hammer curl*. If you've had wrist, elbow, or shoulder problems, the hammer curl may be the variation that feels the most comfortable. The hammer curl may be performed standing (illustrated), seated at the end of a horizontal bench, or seated on an incline bench.

7. DEADLIFT

Four forms of the deadlift will be described:
    basic or conventional deadlift
    parallel-grip deadlift
    partial deadlift
    sumo deadlift

The basic, or conventional deadlift, is what's usually meant by *the deadlift*. Any specification of *basic,* or *conventional,* for example, isn't usually used. This can, however, lead to confusion, because there are several forms of deadlifting.

Properly done, variations of the deadlift are among the most effective strength-training exercises. But use poor technique, abuse low reps, overtrain, or try to lift weights that are too heavy for you, and you'll hurt yourself with any form of the deadlift.

Before you can deadlift with correct technique, you need to be flexible enough to adopt the necessary positioning. You especially need to have supple calves, hamstrings, thigh adductors, and buttocks.

If you've had a serious back injury, don't deadlift without the clearance of a chiropractor. If you've had any minor back injuries, *still* get a chiropractor's clearance.

"Flat back" confusion

The spine is curved when seen from the side. This curvature is the natural, strong structure for absorbing and distributing stress efficiently. When the curves are lost, the strong, load-bearing capability is diminished.

"Keep a flat back" is a common admonition when lifting a weight, and one that I used in my earlier writing. It's not, however, an accurate one. What it really means, is, "Don't round your lower back." Although it may look like the lower back is flat at the bottom of a correctly performed deadlift or squat, as examples, this is an illusion. When contracted, the spinal erectors, if sufficiently developed, may fill the required slight hollow in the lower back's profile at those bottom positions, giving an impression that the lower back is flat, but the actual *lower spine* should be slightly concave, or hollow.

It's the strong contraction of the lumbar musculature that produces the desired, concave lower back, to create a bracing effect. The strong contraction of the muscles on both sides of the spine not only prevents the forward rounding of the back, but helps prevent sideways, asymmetrical bending as well.

If the lower spine is truly flat, the upper back will be rounded, which is a dangerous position when lifting a challenging weight (or even a light one in many cases). A spine that's intentionally straightened while under heavy load bearing is a weakened one that's exposed to an increased risk of injury. A spine that's naturally straight suggests pathology.

When lifting a weight, inside or outside of the gym, keep your shoulders retracted, hips pushed back (extended), and lower back slightly hollowed. There are exceptions, however. For example, during the back extension the back *should* round, and during crunches the lower back shouldn't be hollow—keep it flat against the floor.

How to improve your ability to deadlift

To be able to deadlift competently in any of the four variations described in this book, you need to work at deadlifting technique *and* the essential supportive work. (For most trainees, the conventional deadlift is the most technically demanding of the four variations, and the partial deadlift the least.) There are three major components of good deadlifting ability:

1. The flexibility to be able to *adopt* the correct body positioning.

2. The back strength to be able to *maintain* the correct back positioning.

3. Correct exercise technique.

You need sufficient flexibility in the major musculature of your lower body. Follow the flexibility program in this book. If any of the muscles have anything less than at least a normal, healthy level of flexibility, deadlifting technique will probably be compromised, with a reduction in safety and productivity. Deadlift correctly, or not at all.

You need sufficient strength throughout your back—lower, middle, and upper—to be able to hold your lower back in the required slightly hollowed position during the deadlift. This is critical for safety. The back must not round while deadlifting. Four key back exercises—deadlift itself, back extension, row, and shrug—will help build the required back strength *if* they are worked with correct form, and progressive resistance.

It may take several months before correct deadlifting technique can be implemented, even with minimal weight. Don't be frustrated to begin with. As your flexibility and back strength improve, and your ability to *use* them, so will your deadlifting ability. Until you can adopt the correct technique, keep the resistance very light.

As your deadlifting weight grows, so should your strength in the back extension, row, and shrug, to help you maintain correct back positioning.

Footwear reminder

Especially for deadlifts, squats, and overhead presses, you should not wear shoes with thick or spongy soles and heels.

Get yourself a sturdy pair of shoes with good grip to the floor, arch support, and which minimizes deformation when you're lifting heavy weights. No heel elevation relative to the balls of your feet is especially important for deadlifts and squats.

CRITICAL note for ALL forms of deadlifting

The greater the extent of the forward lean, the greater the risk to the back because of the increased chance of losing the concave lower spine that's essential for safe deadlifting. To try to minimize the risk from deadlifting, keep your maximum forward lean to about 45 degrees from an imaginary vertical line. There has to be forward lean in order to heavily involve the back musculature, but excessive forward lean must be avoided. *A concave lower spine must be maintained.*

Basic or conventional deadlift

Main muscles worked

spinal erectors, multifidii, buttocks, quadriceps, hamstrings, latissimus dorsi, upper back, forearms

Capsule description

with knees well bent and positioned between your hands, and a slightly hollowed lower back, lift the resistance from the floor

Set-up

Once you have the required strength, deadlift using a bar with a 45-pound or 20-kilo plate on each end. Until you have this strength, or if you have to use smaller-diameter plates, set the plates on blocks of wood so that the height of the bar from the floor is the same as it would be *if* it was loaded with full-size plates. Alternatively, use a power rack and set it up so that the bar, when set across the pins, is at the height it would be if it was loaded with full-size plates on the floor or platform.

For best control of the bar, don't train on a slick surface or bare concrete, or the bar will move around when set down, and there's also the chance that your feet will slip. Deadlift on non-slip rubber matting, or construct a simple deadlifting surface through affixing hard-wearing, non-slip carpet to the top side of a 7-foot x 3-foot x 1-inch piece of wood.

Stance

Place your feet about hip-width apart, with toes turned out somewhat. Your hands should just touch the outside of your legs at the bottom of the exercise. Fine-tune the heel spacing and degree of toe flare to find the stance that helps your lifting technique the most. A slightly different stance may help you to deliver more efficient deadlifting technique, because of improved leverage.

Find a foot placement that spreads the stress of the deadlift over your thighs, buttocks, and back. Don't try to focus most of the stress on a single body structure. You must deadlift without your lower back rounding, or your torso leaning forward excessively. Your feet should be firmly planted to the floor, with your heels flat against it. You should feel stable at all times, with no tendency to topple forward or rearward. And push largely through your heels, not the front of your

Start, midpoint, and finish of a correctly performed basic or conventional deadlift.

feet. Furthermore, your knees should point in the same direction as your feet. Don't let your knees buckle inward as you ascend.

Neither stand too far from the bar, nor too close. If you pull the bar into your shins on the ascent, you probably started too close to it. If you're too far from the bar, it will travel away from your shins and you'll place excessive strain on your lower back, risk losing the rep and, perhaps, injure yourself. Position yourself so that the bar brushes against your legs and thighs throughout the ascent. Find the foot positioning that has the bar touching your shins when your knees are bent at the bottom position. But when you're standing erect before descending to get set for the first rep, your shins may be a little away from the bar.

Closely related to how near you stand to the bar, is your arm positioning. Your arms and forearms should hang in a vertical line, and there should be no bending at your elbows. Your arms and forearms should be vertical or near vertical throughout the lift—they link your torso to the bar.

For symmetrical technique you must have symmetrical foot positioning. Each foot must be exactly the same distance from the bar. Even if one foot is just slightly ahead or behind the other, relative to the bar, this will produce an asymmetrical drive and a slight twisting action.

The bar must be parallel with a line drawn across the toes of your shoes. If the bar torques slightly and touches one lower limb but is an inch or two in front of the other, the stress on one side of your body increases substantially, as does the risk of injury.

Grip

A secure grip is especially important for all forms of the deadlift. To aid your grip, use bars with knurling. Smooth bars hinder the grip.

A reverse grip produces asymmetrical distribution of stress, and torque. A correct pronated grip produces symmetrical stress, but isn't as secure as a reverse grip. A bar slipping out of one hand, regardless of the grip used, can result in a lot of torque. If you can't hold onto a bar, don't try to lift it.

As a beginner, a pronated grip should be fine. Use of chalk or rosin on your hands, when required, will help strengthen your grip. If, despite this action, your grip still isn't adequate, use a reverse grip and continue to use chalk or rosin. Use a reverse grip only for your work sets, and alternate from set to set which way around you have your hands. For one set, have your left hand under and right hand over, and the next set have your right hand under and your left hand over. In this way you'll avoid applying the asymmetrical stress in the same way, so that both sides of your body get their turns.

The start

With your feet and the bar in the correct positions, stand and get ready for the first rep. Straighten your elbows and place your hands at your sides ready to drop down into position on the bar. Pull your shoulders back, take your final breath, hold it, and lock your back. Descend with a synchronized bend of your knees *and* forward lean of your torso. Sit down *and* back, and push your hips to the rear. Maintain a slightly hollowed back. Descend until your hands touch the bar (on the knurled area). Keep your bodyweight primarily over your heels, but don't rock back and lose your balance.

If you have to fiddle to get your grip spacing right on the bar, you risk losing the rigid torso and slightly hollowed lower back required for a safe pull. Learn to get your grip right without fiddling around. To help here, get two pieces of garden hose about an inch long each. Slice them open and tape one in the correct position on each side of the bar so that when your hands brush against them, your hands are in the right position. In this way you won't need to look down and then have to re-set your back before the ascent. Instead, descend, keep your head up and torso rigid, immediately place your hands into position, stay tight, then start the ascent.

At the bottom position, your knees should be bent, hips much lower than your shoulders, bar against your shins, head up, and

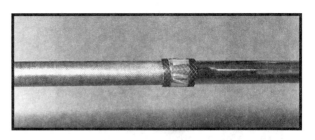

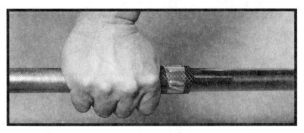

Two pieces of hose appropriately placed on a deadlift bar enable each hand to be positioned without having to look down to check. See text. Here's one of those pieces of hose. For clear viewing, the legs were kept out of the photographs.

your bodyweight felt mostly through your heels. The deadlift is done by the thighs and back *together*.

If you start the deadlift primarily with your thighs, your knees will straighten too quickly and your back will then bear the brunt of the load. If you start the deadlift with little thigh involvement, you won't get far unless it's a light weight for you.

Hold the relative positions of your head, shoulders, and hips during the lift—keep your back slightly hollowed throughout, and shoulder blades retracted. *Never* round your back. Leading with your head and shoulders helps to maintain the proper back positioning.

Ascent

The first part of the ascent is to shrug your shoulders vertically against the bar. Although you won't lift the bar unless it's light, this shrug helps to lock your back into the right position for the pull. Stick your chest out, too. Then squeeze the bar off the floor through simultaneously pushing with your thighs—mostly through your heels—and pulling with your back. When you pull, make it smooth and slow. Don't yank at the bar.

Yanking at the bar leads to bending your elbows, moving you forward, raising your hips too quickly, and increasing stress on your back. Your hips must not rise faster than your shoulders.

Once the bar is off the floor and moving, accelerate its speed a little. Push through both your feet with equal force. If you favor one limb,

<table>
<tr><td>

Critical reminder

Photographs alone can't explain correct form. Please don't skip any of the text.

</td></tr>
</table>

you'll produce a dangerous corkscrew-like motion. Think of pushing your feet through the floor. *Keep your shoulders pulled back, scapulae retracted, and chest pushed up and out.*

Never look down as you initiate the pull from the floor. Keep your jaw parallel with the floor, and look forward or slightly up. Don't look down during the course of a rep.

Keep the bar moving next to your legs, or thighs. If necessary, wear something over your shins to prevent abrasions. Never let the bar move away from you—*this is critical.*

Over the final few inches of the ascent, keep your shoulders pulled back, and chest pushed up and out. If your shoulders slump, your back will round, stress on your spine and its musculature will increase greatly, and you'll set yourself up for a serious injury. Part of the reason why the shrug should be included in your training program is to help you to develop the strength required to keep your shoulders pulled back even under stress.

Remain *vertical* at the top of the lift. If you lean back at the top of the deadlift, that would cause dangerous compression of your intervertebral discs.

As you stand, keep your scapulae retracted, lower back hollowed slightly, weight felt mostly through your heels, and your shoulders, hips, and ankles lined up. Pause for a second, then start the descent.

Exhale on the ascent, and inhale at the top or during the descent.

Descent with the bar

Lowering a straight bar can be awkward, depending on your body structure. Keep your shoulder blades retracted, and chest pushed up and out, as you lower the bar slowly and symmetrically, with a synchronized bend of your knees *and* forward lean of your torso. Sit down *and* back, and push your hips to the rear. Always maintain a slightly hollowed back.

For the descent with a straight bar, slide the bar down your thighs to your knees, through bending at your knees *and* leaning forward. Lean forward the minimum required to get the bar around your knees. Then bend further at your knees and lower the bar to the floor. As soon as the bar is below your knees, keep it as close to your shins as possible, to reduce stress on your lower back. Descend slowly, to keep correct control over the bar—take three to four seconds for the descent.

Once the weight gently touches the floor or platform, immediately start the next rep through shrugging hard on the bar just prior to trying to push your feet into the floor.

Once you've built up the weight so that it's challenging, take a pause for a couple of seconds at the bottom of each rep. But keep your hands in position, torso tensed and tight, lower back slightly hollowed, and eyes looking forward. Breathe as required, then begin the next rep.

Other tips

While experimenting to find your optimum stance, and while using a very light weight, stand on cardboard when you deadlift. When you've settled on your stance, draw around your feet with a marker. Then next session, stand on your footprints and you'll know where you were positioned last time. If you revise your positioning, draw a new pair of footprints. Eventually, you'll settle on a stance that works best for you. Mark that position on cardboard, and refer to it when required.

For work sets once the weight becomes demanding, use chalk or rosin on your hands to improve your grip on the bar, and use a bar with deep knurling. Then through combining specialized grip work and gradual weight increases in the deadlift, you should be able to hold securely any weight you can deadlift. Wrist straps are crutches that promote a weak grip—avoid them.

Always deadlift with collars on the bar. This is critical for keeping the plates in position, and a balanced bar.

Don't bounce the weights on the floor. Gently set the weights on the floor or platform. If you rush the reps, you'll risk banging the floor with the plates on one or both sides. This will disrupt your balance, produce asymmetrical pulling, and stress your body unevenly. This is dangerous.

Never turn your head while you lift or lower the bar, or otherwise the bar will tip somewhat, your lifting groove will be marred, and you could hurt yourself.

If you can't complete a rep without your shoulders slumping, dump the weight. End the set of your own volition before you get hurt.

Common errors—DANGER

Hips too low in the set-up position.

Hips too high, excessive forward lean, loss of correct back set.

Hips have moved too fast in the ascent, and the degree of forward lean has been exaggerated.

Loss of back set during the lockout.

Leaning back during the lockout.

Warning

The photographs on these two pages illustrate common errors that turn the deadlift from one of the most effective exercises, to one of the most dangerous. Deadlift correctly, or not at all.

Loss of back set, and rounding of the back.

More exaggerated rounding of the back.

Legs have locked out too fast, and the bar has drifted away from the legs.

Never drop the weight, even if you have to dump it because you feel your back about to start rounding. Protecting the equipment and floor is only part of the reason for lowering the bar with control. A bar slamming on the floor or platform, or rack pins, can injure your back, shoulders, elbows, or wrists. Lowering the weight too quickly can also lead to rounding the back and losing the important slightly arched lower back.

Once you're training hard, never work the deadlift to failure. Keep the "do or die" rep in you.

Don't deadlift while your lower back is still sore from an earlier workout, or heavy manual labor. Rest a day or two longer, until the soreness has gone.

As seen from the side view, get feedback from an assistant, or record yourself with a video camera. Discover your actual hip, shoulder and head positions. The technique you think you use may not be what you actually use.

Once you've mastered deadlifting technique, don't become overconfident. Just a slight slip of concentration can lead to lowering the bar slightly out of position, for example This will mar your groove, make the weight feel heavier, make the reps harder, and risk injury.

Deadlifts cause callus buildup on your hands. If this is excessive, your skin may become vulnerable to cracks and tears. Both may temporarily restrict your training. Avoid excessive build-up of calluses. Once a week, after you've showered or bathed, use a pumice stone or callus file and gently rub the calluses on your hands. Don't cut the calluses with a blade or scissors. Keep the calluses under control so that they don't cause loss of elasticity on the skin under and around them. To help maintain the elasticity of the skin of your palms and fingers, consume enough essential fatty acids.

Spotting

Spotting isn't required in the deadlift—*never* perform assisted or forced reps in this exercise, or negative-only reps. An alert and knowledgeable assistant can, however, critique your technique, and help keep it correct.

Use of a belt

Two of the men shown in this section are powerlifters, and wear lifting belts out of habit because they use them when they compete in meets. A lifting belt isn't required for training, however, and some powerlifting competitions don't allow belts or any other support gear.

Build your own natural belt through a strong corset of muscle. Train without a belt. Not wearing a belt HELPS your body to strengthen its core musculature.

Parallel-grip deadlift

Main muscles worked

spinal erectors, multifidii, buttocks, quadriceps, thigh adductors, hamstrings, latissimus dorsi, upper back, forearms

Capsule description

with knees well bent, and a slightly hollowed lower back, lift the resistance from the floor

Properly done, the parallel-grip deadlift is one of the most effective exercises—a big, multi-joint exercise that works most of the musculature in the body, namely the thighs, buttocks, and back. There are a number of pieces of equipment used for performing parallel-grip deadlifts, primarily the trap bar, shrug bar, and dumbbells. The dumbbells are the trickiest to use—they get in the way of the lower limbs, constrain stance width and flare more than the one-piece bars, may prohibit ideal foot positioning, and thus hamper technique. Furthermore, many gyms don't have dumbbells heavy enough for trainees other than beginners. Consequently it's the technique of deadlifting with a one-piece, parallel-grip bar that's described in this section.

Before you can parallel-grip deadlift with correct technique, you need to be flexible enough to adopt the necessary positioning. You especially need flexible calves, hamstrings, thigh adductors, and buttocks.

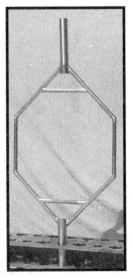

Two examples of parallel-grip bars: the trap bar (left), and the shrug bar.

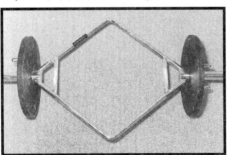

The parallel-grip deadlift. At the bottom position the inward curvature of the model's lower spine is filled with contracted erector spinae muscle, presenting the appearance of a flat back. The trap bar is tipping here, but should be horizontal to the floor.

Set-up

With the parallel-grip deadlift you can involve more knee flexion than in the regular deadlift, hand spacing is determined by the bar's gripping sites (about 22 to 24 inches apart, or 56 to 61 centimeters, depending on the manufacturer), and the bar doesn't drag against your thighs. The pathway of an imaginary straight line joining the ends of the parallel-grip bar can run through your body, rather than in front of it like with a straight bar.

Stance

As a starting point, use a hip-width heel spacing, with your toes turned out about 20 degrees on each side. Fine-tune this to suit you—a little wider, or a little closer. Your legs must fit inside your hands when your hands are on the handles, but without your knees moving inward. Your knees must be in the same plane as your feet. If your feet are too wide, your knees will travel inward to make room for your hands and forearms during the lower part of each rep.

If you can't use this constrained stance safely, the parallel-grip deadlift isn't suited to you. The more roomy inside area of the shrug bar, compared with the trap bar, may provide greater stance options.

The ability to adopt the correct back set is determined primarily by flexibility, back strength, and technique. These take time to develop, for all variations of the deadlift. Progress gradually, as explained in the text. With time, you may be able to adopt a greater range of motion WITHOUT losing the correct back set. It's not necessary to extend the head as much as is shown in this illustration.

With the spacing of your heels determined, place your feet inside the bar in the best position for you. As a starting point, place your feet so that the center of the ends of the bar runs through the bony prominence in the center of the outside of each of your ankles, as you stand with your knees straight.

Although this foot positioning will suit some trainees, for others it may not be ideal. Try it with a light weight, and see. Then, for example, move your feet back an inch, and see how that works. And try an inch forward of the original positioning, too.

Optimal foot positioning is affected by your body structure, and degree of knee flexion. You may need several workouts of practice, and trial and error, before you settle on the optimum foot positioning for you. If you're positioned too far to the rear, you'll probably be bent forward too much and the bar may swing as you lift it off the floor. If you're positioned too far to the front, the bar will probably also swing as you lift it off the floor. There should be no swinging of the bar.

Once you know the foot positioning that works best for you, use a reference point so that you can adopt the right set-up each time. With the trap bar, for example, you could use ankle position relative to an imaginary line running through the ends of the bar. Or, you could use the position of the front rim of your shoes relative to the front of the rhombus. Your eyes must, however, view from the same point each time. For example, as you stand upright, cast your eyes down and perhaps the front rim of your shoes is directly below the inside edge of the front of the rhombus. Perhaps it's an inch inside.

A piece of garden hose of the right size, and appropriately positioned, permits hand centering on a parallel-grip bar's handle without having to look down to check. See text. The legs were kept out of the photographs so as not to obstruct viewing.

Grip

Use a parallel-grip bar with knurling. A smooth bar hinders the grip.

If your hands are off center on the handles, the parallel-grip bar will tip. If only one hand is off center, dangerous rotational stress may result. Keep both hands correctly centered, and the bar parallel with the floor.

Here's how to center your hands on the handles without having to look down and lose the tensed torso and correct get-set position: Slice open two pieces of garden hose, and slip them over each handle, flush against the front bar. Cut the length so that when you feel your hand touching the edge of the hose, your hand is centered. Slip the lengths in position prior to when you parallel-grip deadlift.

Performance

Most of the performance guidelines in the *Basic or conventional deadlift* section apply to the parallel-grip deadlift, including the "Other tips." Please review that material before parallel-grip deadlifting.

Common errors

Left, hips are too high for the starting position, producing excessive forward lean, and loss of the correct back set. Right, following a correct start (not illustrated here) the hips have moved too fast, producing loss of back set, and rounding of the back. The errors illustrated in the previous section, for the conventional deadlift, also apply to the parallel-grip deadlift except for hip depth in the starting position. For the parallel-grip deadlift the hips can safely start at a lower position, provided the back is correctly set, and the range of motion is safe for the knees.

With the conventional deadlift, the problem of getting a straight bar around the knees is what produces the increased forward lean and reduced knee flexion compared with the parallel-grip deadlift. With the latter, you're inside the bar as against behind it with the straight-bar deadlift. This is what permits the reduced forward lean and increased knee flexion in the parallel-grip deadlift, and potentially makes it a safer exercise.

Here's the torso set you need to fight to maintain throughout the parallel-grip deadlift: While standing, take a big breath, keep a high chest, tense your upper-back muscles, and rotate your shoulders back into a military posture. This will tend to push your arms out away from your body, as your lats will be hard. Your lower back will be slightly hollowed, or concave.

Start the descent with a synchronized bending of your knees *and* forward lean of your torso. Sit down *and* back, and push your hips to the rear. Always maintain a slightly hollowed lower back, and keep your shoulder blades retracted.

Guide the bar, don't just lower it. With a straight-bar deadlift, the bar should brush your shins or thighs throughout the movement, but in the parallel-grip deadlift, here's the general guideline: Your hands should follow a line along the center of your femurs and, further down, along the center of the sides of your calves. When your hands are at knee height, they should also be in line with your knees. If your hands get behind that line, you risk being too upright. Your hands may, however, be a little forward of that line.

At the bottom of each rep, rather than pull on the bar, focus on trying to push your feet into the floor while maintaining the correct torso set.

The parallel-grip deadlift can increase thigh involvement further if it's done from a raised surface. The two critical provisos are that your lower back can be kept slightly hollow in this extended range of motion, and you have no knee limitations. To try a raised surface, start with no more than one inch. If, after a few weeks, all is well— correct technique maintained, with no knee or back problems— perhaps try a further half inch, and so on, up to a maximum of two to three inches.

Two 15-kilo plates, smooth sides up, can be placed side-by-side under a parallel-grip bar, to produce a raised, stable surface from which to deadlift for increased quadriceps involvement provided that the correct back set is maintained, and the increased range of motion is safe for the trainee.

Use of dumbbells for the parallel-grip deadlift can work provided you have access to dumbbells heavy enough to provide adequate resistance. But if the dumbbells are touched to the floor or platform on each rep, there's a potential problem because of the small-diameter plates—increased range of motion relative to that with a trap bar or shrug bar with 45-pound or 20-kilo plates on it. Elevate the dumbbells on strong boxes or crates so that the range of motion isn't excessive for you. Never descend beyond the point where your lower back loses the required slightly hollowed position.

Performing the parallel-grip deadlift in an exaggeratedly upright manner, to further increase stress on the quadriceps, should be

This home-gym trainee is using plates of smaller diameter than the usual 20-kilo or 45-pound ones. Such plates lead to an exaggerated range of motion that's unsafe for many trainees. By using a pair of platforms—for example, as illustrated—the range of motion can be reduced as required.

avoided, because of the overly limited back involvement and increased knee stress, which may lead to knee problems. A natural spread of work between the thighs and back produces a balanced division of the stress.

Elevated handles

Some parallel-grip deadlift bars have raised handles, which reduce the range of deadlifting motion when compared with a bar with regular handles (like in the illustrations) and if both bars are loaded with the same diameter plates. The elevated handles may suit you if you can't safely use the full range of motion with 45-pound plates on a regular parallel-grip bar. If you can safely use the full range of motion, but only have access to a bar with raised handles, elevate yourself on a sturdy, non-slip surface the same height as the elevation of the handles, or use smaller-diameter plates.

Partial deadlift

Main muscles worked

spinal erectors, multifidii, buttocks, hamstrings, latissimus dorsi, upper back, forearms

Capsule description

with a slightly hollowed lower back, straight elbows, and slightly bent knees, lift a bar from knee height

The partial deadlift described here is a variation of what's commonly called a *stiff-legged deadlift*. Importantly, the variation is done with a *reduced* range of motion. Some people may call it a *Romanian deadlift*.

The partial deadlift is often used as a substitute for the conventional deadlift for trainees who have safety concerns for their backs because of the greater range of motion of the regular deadlift. Substantial back, buttock, hamstring, and grip involvement remain, but quadriceps involvement is minimized.

Performance

In a power rack find the pin setting that puts the bar at just below your kneecaps when your knees are slightly bent. That's the bottom position. Alternatively, set a loaded bar on boxes at the height so that the bar's starting position is the same as in the rack set-up.

Stand with your feet under the bar, heels about hip-width apart, and feet parallel with each other, or flared a little. Take a shoulder-width or slightly wider overhand grip. For just the first rep, bend your knees more than slightly, to help ensure correct back positioning. Hollow your lower back slightly and, with straight elbows, shrug against the bar and pull your shoulders back, and push your chest up and out. The bar won't move unless the weight is light, but the shrug will lock your lower back into the required, hollowed position. Now, while looking forward or upward, *simultaneously* pull with your back *and* straighten your knees, to move the bar.

During subsequent reps, bend your knees only slightly. Your knees should straighten as you complete the lift, and bend slightly once again during the descent. Keep your head up at all times, shoulder blades retracted, and chest pushed up and out. During the descent, push your hips rearward, to help keep your lower back in the correct hollowed position. The bar should brush your knees or thighs. Don't

lean back at the top. Stand straight, pause for a second, keep your scapulae retracted and lower back hollowed (without exaggeration), then lower the bar to the pins through bending your knees slightly and simultaneously leaning forward.

Don't rest the bar on the pins or boxes at the bottom position. Instead, pause for a second just above the pins. Maintain a locked, hollowed lower back, with your shoulders pulled back. Smoothly move into the next rep.

Exhale during the ascent, or at the top. Either inhale and make the descent, or inhale as you descend.

Lift and lower symmetrically, and don't turn your head. Furthermore, don't let your shoulders round. If your shoulders start to slump, and you can't pull them back, dump the bar instantly but with control.

The exercise can be done with a straight bar, or a parallel-grip bar such as a shrug bar. With a parallel-grip bar, it has to be done from boxes, because the bar isn't long enough for use inside a power rack unless the bar has elongated ends.

Even with chalk or rosin on your hands, and a well-knurled, straight bar, you may eventually be forced to use a reverse grip. If so, alternate which way around you have your hands from set to set.

A lower position for the bottom of the partial deadlift, illustrated outside of a power rack. This trainee—because of his flexibility, strength, and technique—can maintain the correct back set even at this degree of forward lean, and range of motion. But most trainees can't, and thus for safety should use a lesser range of motion like that shown on the previous page. Individual leverages—torso and limb lengths, and their relative proportions—affect performance in deadlift variations, and other exercises. Some trainees are better constucted to perform a given exercse than are other trainees.

It's not necessary to extend the head as much as is shown in this photo.

FULL-RANGE, stiff-legged deadlift—*DANGER*

The full-range, stiff-legged deadlift is hazardous. Instead, use less risky but effective exercises for your hamstrings, buttocks, and back, which are the primary areas worked by the full-range, stiff-legged deadlift. The recommended exercises employed for these areas are the conventional deadlift, parallel-grip deadlift, partial deadlift, sumo deadlift, leg curl, and back extension. Of course, these exercises must be performed correctly if they are to be safe.

The further the torso leans forward, the more difficult it is to maintain the proper set position of the back, where the lower back is slightly hollowed. The full-range, stiff-legged deadlift takes the forward lean to an extreme, where the lower back rounds. This massively increases the stress on the various structures of the back, and greatly increases the risk of injury. Back rounding is important for working the spinal musculature, but it should take place in back extensions, *not* in any form of the deadlift, whether with bent knees or straight knees.

The stiff-legged deadlift to the floor, and the stiff-legged deadlift while standing on a box. The former is the most common form of the full-range, stiff-legged deadlift, but it's sometimes done on an elevated surface for an even greater range of motion. For safety, BOTH SHOULD BE AVOIDED. Notice the back rounding, and severe loss of back set. But the partial, stiff-legged deadlift described on the previous pages is a safe, effective exercise if performed correctly.

Sumo deadlift

Main muscles worked

spinal erectors, multifidii, buttocks, quadriceps, thigh adductors, hamstrings, latissimus dorsi, upper back, forearms

Capsule description

with knees well bent and positioned outside your hands, and a slightly hollowed lower back, lift the resistance from the floor

The sumo deadlift uses a straight bar, but because of the widened stance relative to that used in the regular deadlift, and the hands positioned *between* the legs, the back may be more upright in the sumo deadlift when comparing the two styles on the *same* trainee. There'll probably be more knee flexion to balance the more upright torso. Although the back is heavily involved in the sumo deadlift, the buttocks *and* thighs take relatively more stress.

The sumo and conventional deadlifts are similar in performance and pathway of the bar. It's the different stance that distinguishes the sumo deadlift. The grip used in the sumo deadlift may be a little closer.

Your knees may be less of an obstacle to get around in the sumo deadlift, which is why you'll probably bend forward to a lesser degree in the sumo deadlift than in the conventional style.

Sumo-style powerlifters may benefit from an extreme width of stance that has their feet almost touching the plates. This reduces the range of motion to the minimum. But for general training, an extreme stance isn't desirable. Use a moderately wide stance.

For example, if you're about 5-10 tall, use a stance with about 22 to 24 inches or 56 to 61 centimeters between your heels as the starting point, with your toes turned out at about 45 degrees. Fine-tune from there. Try the same flare but a slightly wider stance. Then try a little less flare but the same stance. Keep fine-tuning until you find what helps your technique the most. After a few weeks of experience you may want to fine-tune your stance further.

Find the foot positioning relative to the bar that, when your knees are bent at the bottom position, has the bar touching your shins. But when you're standing erect prior to descending to take the bar for the first rep, your shins may be a little away from the bar.

For the first descent, follow the same format as given for the conventional deadlift. Descend until your hands touch the bar, then take your grip. Don't grip the bar so closely that your hands are on

Bottom and midpoint of the sumo deadlift (left), and bottom and top position of the sumo deadlift (right). The former shows a wider stance than the latter.

the smooth part of the bar. Use a hip-width grip as a starting point, with your hands on the knurling, and fine-tune from there. If your grip is too close, you'll find it difficult to control the bar's balance.

For the drive from the floor, ascent, lockout, descent, and breathing, follow the same guidelines as in the conventional deadlift.

Don't immediately introduce intensive, wide-stance deadlifting, because that would be a road to injury. Take several weeks to progressively work into the wide stance, using a weight that doesn't tax you. Stretching for your thigh adductors, hamstrings, and buttocks may be needed, to give you the flexibility to adopt your optimum stance. Once you've mastered the technique, *then* progressively add resistance.

8. FINGER EXTENSION

Main muscles worked

finger extensors

Capsule description

against resistance, open all the digits of the hand

The finger extension is an important exercise. It strengthens the muscles that extend the fingers, whereas exercises that involve the grip work the muscles that flex the fingers. A strength imbalance between these opposing muscles can cause elbow problems.

Manual resistance

Put the digits of your right hand together. Put the tips of the fingers (and thumb) of your left hand on the outside ends of the corresponding digits of the other hand. Open your right hand against resistance provided by your left hand. Allow the finger joints to bend sufficiently to produce a full range of movement.

Once you're working the exercise hard, following a period of gradual adaptation, perform a warm-up set for each hand with minimal resistance. Then perform the work sets with enough resistance to make each rep taxing. Apply resistance against the fingers as they open *and* close—positive phase and negative phase, respectively. Provide more resistance during the negative phase. Perform each rep smoothly, over a full range of motion.

Another method, while seated, is to place the tips of your right hand together, and put your hand between your lower thighs, with your wrist turned so that your right thumb is against your right inner thigh. Keep all your digits straight, and spread the load evenly over all of them. Find the precise positioning of your hand that permits this. Perform each rep smoothly, over a full range of motion, with enough resistance from your thighs to make each rep taxing on the positive and negative phases.

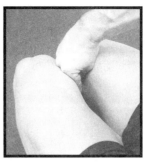
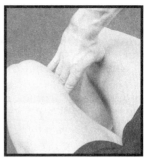

Thigh-assisted, manual finger extension. Try with feet together, and feet hip-width apart. The latter may enable you to apply resistance with greater control.

The manual finger extension doesn't permit measurable resistance. Over time, however, gradually increase the manual resistance.

Band resistance

For measurable resistance, get some elastic bands that are about three inches or eight centimeters long when not stretched. Take just one of them, to learn the exercise. Put all five digits of your right hand inside the elastic band so that the band rests approximately on the joints nearest your finger nails. Smoothly stretch out your fingers as far as you can without the elastic band slipping down. Find the degree of curvature in your fingers needed to keep the elastic band in place throughout the exercise.

Find elastic bands of various strengths so that you can add gradual resistance. Regularly replace the bands because, with use, they lose strength and elasticity.

To help keep the bands in position, twist them around your middle finger before putting your other digits inside the bands. This will increase the tension on the bands and reduce the number of them you can use, unless you switch to longer bands.

The Metolius "GripSaver Plus" is a ready-made device for finger extension, designed specifically for rehab or prevention of climbing-related finger, wrist, and elbow injuries. It's an alternative to elastic bands, although it doesn't provide variable resistance.

www.metoliusclimbing.com

9. HAND-GRIPPER WORK

Main muscles worked

finger flexion muscles, forearms

Capsule description

crush the hand gripper's handles together

Hand-gripper work is optional, but recommended. Gripper training will strengthen your grip and hands beyond what your general training will produce, and perhaps build forearm musculature, too. And many trainees find gripper training especially enjoyable. It can be done at home, with your own grippers.

Grippers are inexpensive—see *Resources*. The ones with knurled, metal handles—torsion-spring grippers—start at under 100 pounds closing strength, and go up to over 300 pounds. The ability to close a gripper of 200 pounds rating is rare. The ability to close a gripper of 300 pounds is phenomenal. Ideally, initially get a gripper under 100 pounds, and two or three with the smallest increments in resistance thereafter. You may need to use more than one manufacturer, to obtain a gradual progression in resistance.

Although different manufacturers produce torsion-spring grippers that are claimed to have the same closing strengths, the actual strength ratings may be different, because of variations in construction, and the springs. And the same manufacturer's grippers may vary in strength from batch to batch. For example, a gripper with a rating of 140 pounds may be more like 150 pounds, for example, whereas another with a 140-pound rating may be more like 130 pounds.

Get grippers that have handles spaced no more than ten centimeters or four inches between the bottom, outside edges. Some grippers are significantly wider than this, which makes them difficult to handle, especially if you have small hands.

You may need to start with a gripper that has plastic grips, which sporting goods stores sell. This has a rating of no more than about 50 pounds. When you can do at least 20 full closes with it, with a pause on each crush, move to the lowest-strength torsion-spring gripper.

With the Ivanko super gripper, however, just one is required to produce resistances from about 50 pounds closing strength, to over 300, and the resistance can be adjusted in small, gradual increments.

Torsion-spring gripper

Look at the spring or wire of a torsion-spring gripper. There are two sides, where each goes into a handle. One side of the spring is perfectly curved. The other side has a slight ridge in

The dogleg is shown on the right side of the left torsion-spring gripper. For the right photograph, another gripper has been turned over to show the non-dogleg side on the right.

it—this is the "dogleg." Always put the dogleg side into the thumb side of your hand, for consistency. The gripper may also be a little less difficult to close that way around.

With the gripper in your right palm, dogleg side nearest your thumb, thrust your thumb forward and position the dogleg handle at or just in front of the fold in your palm that marks the start of your thumb mound. Then set the gripper by using your left index finger and thumb to pinch the handles of the gripper just sufficiently so that you can wrap the finger tips of your right three longer fingers around the handle, with your right little finger lined up to be about half off the bottom edge of the handle. This set-up position maximizes leverage. Remove your left hand from the gripper, and put your right little finger in position. Keep all four parallel fingers touching one another—don't spread them. The little finger isn't long enough to go around the handle in the starting position, but will move around during the crush, and contribute then.

How much you need to pinch the handles to get into the starting position depends on the spacing of the handles, and your hand size. Avoid excessively spaced handles.

Using a gripper you can close fully, experiment to find your strongest starting position. A small change in where the gripper rests in your palm, and in how your fingers are placed on the handle, can make a significant difference in your ability to close the gripper.

Once properly set in the starting position, crush the handles together. As you crush, thrust your thumb forward, to increase its involvement. Hold the crushed position for a second or two, then return to the starting position.

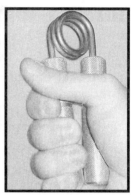

When back in the starting position, pause for a moment without losing the correct set—this means not opening the gripper fully, because that would take you beyond the correct starting position—and then perform the next rep. Complete the set, and change hands. If you're doing singles, perform just one rep, then change hands. Take a brief rest, perform another single for each hand, and so on.

If you can shut the gripper fully, you'll hear the handles click together. During the brief pause at full closure, grind the handles together.

You may not be able to close the gripper fully, depending on its strength relative to yours. If you can't shut the gripper, briefly hold the maximum degree of closure, then let the gripper open to the starting position. Work on increasing the degree of closure, as the weeks and months go by.

Negative reps can be helpful in gripper training, especially using a gripper that you can't close without assistance. Push the handles together with the assistance of your other hand (and your torso), or push the gripper against your thigh as you squeeze. With the gripper shut, or as near shut as you can manage, try to crush it as the gripper opens. Don't merely try to slow the gripper's opening. Month to month, increase the duration of the negatives, and the degree of closure if you can't fully close it now, even with assistance.

During all forms of gripper work, breathe freely. *Don't hold your breath.*

Take it easy for the first few weeks, to condition your hands to the rigors of gripper work. If you try to rush your progress, you'll risk injury to your finger muscles and joints, and damage to your skin.

If your hands slip on the handles, use chalk or rosin. If the knurling is overly sharp and cuts into your skin, wrap some tape around the handles, or use some emery cloth to take the edge off the knurling. Periodically, use a wire brush to clean the knurling.

Ivanko super gripper

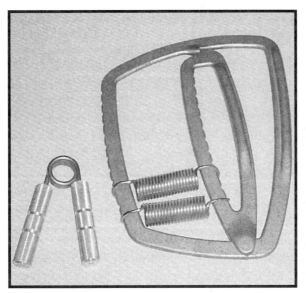

Comparison of a torsion-spring hand gripper, and the Ivanko super gripper. The springs on the Ivanko unit are set in the slots of least resistance for two springs: 1 and 3—the springs can't fit in adjacent slots.

Comparison of the springs of 70-pound and 300-pound strength torsion-spring grippers.

The Ivanko super gripper has twelve slots for positioning two springs. This yields over 100 different possible resistance settings, to cater for all levels of gripping strength, and to permit progress in small increments.

Furthermore, it has a large handle that permits you to use two hands to position the gripper while setting up for negative reps, and for sustained, single holds.

The large handle is also helpful for fine-tuning resistance. The lower your hand is on the handle—the closer your hand is to the pivot point—the harder it is to close the gripper. If, for example, you can close the gripper at one setting with your hand at the outermost position on the handle, but are unable to close it at the next setting, you can stay at the lower setting for a while longer but increase its resistance a little (but not as much as it would be at the next setting) by using a lower hand position on the handle. Build your strength a bit further at the lower setting, and then move to the next setting but with your hand in the outermost position.

You may experience slippage on the Ivanko handle, because it has a smooth finish. Slippage can be prevented by wrapping some tape with high friction around the handle.

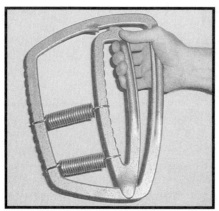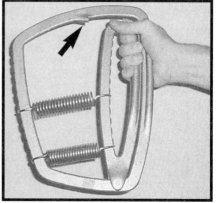

Note the protrusion on the inside, upper rim of the Ivanko super gripper, which prevents the handle opening excessively and the springs losing their tension.

Position the outer part of the unit at or just in front of the fold in your palm that marks the start of your thumb mound. Wrap the tips of your fingers around the moving part. You may need to use your disengaged hand to help get set for the first rep of a set. Smoothly close the handle until the moving unit strikes the fixed outermost structure, hold the contact for a moment, and then smoothly release. Breathe freely. Don't hold your breath.

When back in the starting position, pause without losing the correct set—this means not opening the gripper fully, because that would take you beyond the correct starting position—and then perform the next rep. If you're doing singles, perform one rep, then change hands.

Release the handle gradually and smoothly after each close—for the best training effect, and to maintain the set-up of the springs. If the release is fast, the moving unit may miss the stop protrusion on the gripper that limits the range of motion. If that happens, the springs will loosen and slip out of position, and need to be re-positioned.

Take it easy for the first few weeks, to condition your hands to the rigors of gripper work. If you try to rush your progress, you'll risk injury to your finger muscles and joints. The Ivanko unit isn't knurled, so it doesn't cause the skin friction that the torsion-spring grippers do.

Between training sessions, keep tension off the springs by slipping the moveable part off the stop protrusion. If the gripper is stored under tension, the springs will slacken with time.

For all hand-gripper work, keep your elbow flexed. This reduces the strain in and around the elbow compared to doing the grip work with a fully extended elbow.

Here are 40 of the possible settings of the Ivanko super gripper, arranged in order of the force required to close the gripper at those settings. Use this so that you can increase resistance in small, gradual increments. These settings and poundages are given by S. Stamp, at www.ivanko.com/products/html_stuff/gripper_info.html

The exact poundages at these settings may vary across different batches of the super gripper, and according to the condition of the springs, but the sequence will still produce the required gradual progression.

The first two numbers show the slots that the springs are positioned in to produce the resistance shown in the third number. For example, 3-1-45 means that when the springs are positioned in the third and first pairs of slots, about 45 pounds of force is required to close the handle.

3	1	45 pounds	9	5	182 pounds
4	1	56 pounds	11	1	185 pounds
4	2	64 pounds	4	10	191 pounds
5	1	70 pounds	9	6	197 pounds
5	2	77 pounds	3	11	203 pounds
6	1	85 pounds	12	1	211 pounds
6	2	92 pounds	9	7	214 pounds
7	1	101 pounds	2	12	219 pounds
7	2	109 pounds	5	11	228 pounds
6	4	113 pounds	7	10	235 pounds
8	1	120 pounds	6	11	242 pounds
8	2	128 pounds	5	12	253 pounds
8	3	137 pounds	7	11	259 pounds
9	1	140 pounds	6	12	268 pounds
7	5	143 pounds	8	11	278 pounds
8	4	149 pounds	7	12	285 pounds
9	3	157 pounds	9	11	298 pounds
1	10	162 pounds	8	12	303 pounds
9	4	169 pounds	9	12	323 pounds
8	6	177 pounds	12	10	345 pounds

Keep accurate records of the spring settings you use.

It may take months of consistent training to progress from one entry-level, torsion-spring gripper to the next, provided there's a gradual progression of resistance across the grippers. If the jump between grippers is large, it may take over a year, or forever, to progress from one gripper to the next. With a single, inexpensive Ivanko super gripper you can progress in small increments, from little resistance, to a great deal.

10. LATERAL RAISE

Main muscles worked

deltoids, especially the medial or side head, trapezius

Capsule description

with a vertical torso, lift the resistance to your sides until your elbows are just above your shoulders

The lateral raise is a valuable exercise because, in addition to working the deltoids and trapezius, it works a number of small muscles around the shoulders that are involved in abduction of the humerus. Strengthening these muscles helps to keep the shoulders healthy.

Dumbbell lateral raise

Stand with your feet about hip-width apart, a dumbbell in each hand at the side of your thighs, palms facing your thighs. With your scapulae pulled back, head up, and elbows slightly bent for comfort, raise your hands to about chin height. Pause, then lower the dumbbells under control. Keep your palms facing the floor in a neutral position—don't turn your wrists so that your thumbs move forward or rearward. Furthermore, keep your wrists neutral—don't flex or extend them.

Take about three seconds for the ascent, pause for a second at the top, take a further three seconds to lower the dumbbells, pause for another second, then move into the next rep. Keep your torso and head upright at all times—don't lean forward or rearward. Don't crane your head, or move it to the rear or one side— keep your head in a neutral position. Keep your weight evenly distributed over your feet. Furthermore, don't let the dumbbells drift forward. Exhale on the ascent, inhale on the descent.

The lateral raise may be performed one side at a time. Brace your non-working hand on a stable object, and keep your torso upright. Reverse the set-up to work the other side.

There are three variations that aren't illustrated. The

lateral raise may be performed seated—for example, on the end of a bench, with feet on the floor. It may also be done while sitting against an incline bench set at about 75 degrees, facing *into* the bench.

Although not illustrated, the lateral raise may be done one arm at a time while lying *sideways* against an incline bench set no higher than at about 45 degrees. Raise your arm to just above head height. This variation heavily stresses the deltoids at the bottom of the exercise, whereas the other lateral raises heavily stress the deltoids at the top.

Machine lateral raise

Follow the manufacturer's guidelines for the set-up. This may mean setting the height of the seat so that your shoulders line up with the pivot points. The correct set-up position is important, for joint care and the desired effect on the deltoids.

Perform the exercise with a controlled movement—about three seconds for the ascent, pause for a second at the top, another three seconds for the descent, a further pause for a second at the bottom, and so on. Keep your torso upright, shoulders retracted, chest out, and head in a neutral position. And apply the force through the pads alongside your elbows, not through the handles. Applying force through your hands may cause shoulder irritation. Grip the handles *lightly*.

II. LEG CURL

Main muscles worked

hamstrings, lower back

Capsule description

with resistance against your heels, lift your heels toward your hips

The leg curl provides direct exercise for the hamstrings—the three muscles of the rear thighs. This is important for developing healthy, balanced musculature around the knees and hips. There are also aesthetic benefits—a curve to the rear thigh, which in turn helps offset the protrusion of the buttocks.

Set-up

Lie face-down on a leg curl bench. The bench shouldn't be flat, but have a hump where your hips are placed. Place your heels beneath the resistance pad. It's essential that you line your knees up correctly— center of your knees in line with the center of the pivot point of the machine. The correct set-up will have your kneecaps positioned *just* over the edge of the bench—not on the bench itself.

Where the resistance pads are positioned is adjustable on some machines. If you use an adjustable machine, set the resistance pads so that they are flush with your ankles when your knees are straight and in the correct position.

If you use a machine with a range-of-motion limitation control, set it at the fullest safe setting for you. You would need to experiment, with minimal resistance, to find what this range of motion is for you. If there's no range-of-motion control, do it yourself—don't lower your heels all the way down to the position of straight knees if that's excessive for your knees. Instead, maintain a slight degree of flexion even at the bottom (starting) position—an inch or two short of your knees being straight.

If you use a selectorized leg curl machine you may be able to delimit the range of motion manually. Remove the pin from the weight stack, then grip the cable that's attached to the guide rod that runs through the weight stack, and lift it. The top weight plate will rise alone, revealing the guide rod. Expose two holes on the rod, for example, then use the pin to select the required weight. The gap between the

first and second weight plates indicates the reduction in range of motion. Fine-tune the extent of the reduction according to what's required to produce the maximum safe range of motion for you. Make a note in your training log of the setting.

How to manually delimit the range of motion using a selectorized weight stack. See text.

The procedure for delimiting the range of motion in the leg curl can be used for other selectorized machines, when excessive stretching needs to be avoided, such as the machine pullover.

Performance

Grasp the handles or other gripping sites in a symmetrical manner, and hold them lightly—just sufficiently to stabilize yourself. Don't involve your upper body in the leg curl. Keep your hips firmly against the bench, and lift your head and shoulders slightly off the bench. Face forward or to the floor—don't turn your head to the side. Pull your toes toward your shins—opposite of pointing your toes—and keep them in that position throughout the set.

Slowly and smoothly lift your heels as far toward your hips as is comfortable. Hold the position of fullest contraction for a second, then smoothly lower your heels to the starting position. Pause for a second, then repeat. There must be no sudden or jerky movements. Move smoothly up, and smoothly down, about three seconds for each phase, plus a second for the pause at the top, and another second for the pause at the starting position. Exhale on the ascent, inhale on the descent.

During the ascent of your feet, your hips should come off the bench slightly, to permit full contraction of the hamstrings. Your hips should rise no more than one inch. Any more than that will overstress your lower back through excessive extension of your spine, which can cause injury. Excessive lifting of the hips also reduces the work done by your hamstrings.

The start of the rep must be done with great care—ease into it, don't heave the weight. After the final rep, when lowering the weight to its resting place, place it gently.

Options for leg curl machines

Some manufacturers produce leg curl machines for seated or standing work, one leg at a time in some cases. Some provide work for both limbs simultaneously, but each thigh may have independent resistance so each would perform its full share of the work.

The standing leg curl is a unilateral movement that usually leads to technique flaws, including a torso twist, and uneven stresses on the spine and torso from the asymmetrical loading.

If there's more than one leg curl machine where you train, find the one that feels best for you. For trainees with back problems, the prone and standing leg curls may irritate the back even when done with correct technique. Try the seated version instead. Generally, the seated leg curl is the pick of the machines—for comfort, maintenance of correct technique, and isolation of the hamstrings. During the seated leg curl, however, never press down on your thighs—there should be no exaggerated compression of your hamstrings.

Seated leg curl.

Adding weight

Selectorized cable units, and selectorized machines in general, commonly have weight increments of 10 pounds or 5 kilos, and larger in some cases. This is too much weight to progress by in a single jump. Where you train may have special weights of 5 pounds or 2.5 kilos—and perhaps smaller ones, too—designed to fit on the top of a weight stack. If it doesn't, you may be able to get your own from an exercise equipment store. Use them to help you to work from one pin setting to the next.

Alternatively, place the weight selection pin through a small barbell weight plate before the pin goes into the weight stack. Although a pin that holds a plate won't go fully into the weight stack, it should go through enough to hold the plate securely and select the resistance, too.

Magnetic small plates are another option for adding small increments of weight to a stack.

Whichever option you choose, check that the set-up is secure before you perform a set.

Origin of "hamstrings"

The three thigh muscles of the posterior or rear thigh are usually referred to as the "hamstring" group. This is because tendons of those muscles are used by butchers to attach curing hams to meat hooks.

12. LEG PRESS

Main muscles worked

quadriceps, buttocks, thigh adductors, hamstrings

Capsule description

with your feet against the foot plate, bend and straighten your knees

The leg press can be done seated or lying, depending on the model of machine. Some leg presses, especially the models where the resistance is pushed vertically, are dangerous for many trainees.

For most trainees, the leg press of choice will be of the leverage style—for example, the models produced by Hammer Strength, and the Nautilus XP LOAD Leg Press. If such a machine isn't available, use a 45-degree leg press, which can be found in most well-equipped gyms. The 45-degree leg presses vary according to their design and adjustability. Ideally, they should be adjustable in small increments for knee flexion, and inclination of the back support.

Some leg presses have the foot plate near or at the bottom position when not in use, while other leg presses have the foot plate near or at the top position when not in use.

The involvement of the thigh adductors can be substantial in the leg press. Careful stretching of the adductors is recommended prior to leg pressing.

Set-up and positioning

Center yourself, side to side, on the seat or bench. Place your feet on the middle or, better yet, on the higher part of the foot plate. The lower your feet, the greater the knee stress. Some leg presses have insufficiently sized foot plates. Depending on the model, you may need to position your toes off the top edge of the foot plate, to produce a safe set-up for your knees. But the balls of your feet, and your heels, must be in full contact with the foot plate throughout each set.

A small change of foot spacing or flare can improve knee comfort. Without any plates on the leg press, try a hip-width heel placement, with the inside edges of your feet parallel with each other. Then try turning your toes out a little. Next, try a bit more flare. Then try different heel positioning in the different positions of toe flare. Find the heel spacing and angle of flare that feel the most comfortable for

A type of leverage leg press.

The 45-degree leg press. Above, a good set-up of the feet. Above right, wrong set-up, feet too low and too close, which produces exaggerated stress on the knees. Right, excessive range of motion, resulting in the lower back coming off the back support. The lower back must be supported.

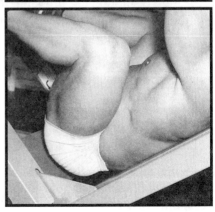

you. The foot positioning must help to keep your knees pointing in the same direction as your toes. Don't let your knees buckle in.

Some leg press machines have foot plates that can be adjusted to find the best angle of fit for the user, but most have a fixed position. If you use an adjustable machine, set the angle of the foot plate so that you can push mostly through your heels throughout each rep. If you don't push mostly through your heels, knee problems may result.

Avoid excessive forward travel of your knees, to minimize stress on those joints. To begin with, keep your knees behind the line of your toes. To judge the position of your knees, view them from the bottom position of a leg press rep. If your knees are ahead of the line of your toes, reduce the forward travel of your knees—move your feet up on the footplate (if there's room), or reduce the depth of motion.

Some leg presses don't have adjustable seat positioning to set the depth of motion, but have an adjustable, delimiting arrangement instead. If the machine isn't adjustable for depth of motion by a built-in means, use some marker of your own to indicate when the carriage is at your safe maximum depth. Place a restraint block in the appropriate place.

If, after two months of building up the resistance there's no negative reaction in your knees, lower back, hips, or anywhere else, finish off each leg press session with one set of a greater range of motion, with a much reduced weight. For that set, increase the depth of motion by about two inches. This will mean that there's more knee flexion, and probably more forward travel of your knees. This may be safe for you, and beneficial.

Provided there's no negative reaction to the increased range of motion, build up the resistance gradually over at least two months until you're using the same weight in the increased range of motion as you were in the lesser range. During that process, drop the lesser-range-of-motion leg pressing. If there's still no negative reaction to the increased range of motion, try a further increase by lowering your feet a little on the foot plate *provided* you can still push mostly through your heels.

But, the increases in range of motion may be limited by the positioning of your lower back. Your lower back must always be fully supported by the seat or bench—there must be no rounding of your lower spine, even if your knees will tolerate a greater range of motion. If your lower back isn't fully supported, your risk of injury will increase greatly.

Some leg presses have back supports that can be adjusted for their degree of incline. If adjustable, select a setting that minimizes compression of your lower back. Try all the settings, with minimal resistance, to discover which setting appears to suit you best. As you progress in the leg press, if you experience discomfort because of compression of your lower back, experiment with a different inclination of back support—perhaps more upright than less upright.

Performance

Keep your head stationary, in a neutral position, and fixed against the head support if one is built into the machine, and it's comfortable to rest against. Hold the machine's hand grips. If there aren't any hand grips, hold rigid parts of the machine clear of the moving carriage.

With your feet flat on the foot plate, correctly positioned for you, push mostly through your heels. Unless the footplate is already at the top position, smoothly and slowly extend your legs to get into the top position ready for the first rep. Never slam into the locked out position. Brake before your knees lock out, and stop the movement half an inch short of the point where your knees are straight. Pause for a second, then start the descent.

For leg presses that start from or just below the top position, carefully lock out your knees and then release the machine's top stops, so that you can perform the descent without obstruction, down to the bottom stops that have been pre-set to suit you. (At the end of a set, with your knees locked out, put the top stops back in position, and gently set the carriage down.)

Lower under control—take about three seconds to make the descent. As you reach the maximum safe depth for you, stay tight, pause for a second, and press out of it. Don't bounce. Do the turnaround slowly and smoothly, without relaxing. And take about three seconds for the extension of your legs—the positive phase of the rep.

Apply force symmetrically, with your legs working in unison. Distribute the stress of the exercise symmetrically over your thighs, hips, and back.

Inhale at the top of each rep, or during the descent, and exhale during the ascent. *Don't hold your breath.*

Other tip

Don't work your lower back intensively immediately before you leg press, because that would reduce your lower back's potential as a stabilizer.

Unilateral leg press

A few leg presses, such as one of the models produced by Hammer Strength, have independent foot plates, one for each foot. These *isolateral* or *unilateral* machines can be used one limb at a time, as against the usual *bilateral* machines that have a single foot plate for *both* feet. A unilateral leg press also gives you the option of working both limbs bilaterally, although each will have its own resistance to deal with. It may, for example, be especially valuable if you have one limb shorter than the other.

If you exercise one limb at a time, keep your non-working limb extended and braced, while your other one completes a set. But a unilateral leg press machine applies asymmetrical and rotational stress to your lower back, because both limbs don't push at the same time *unless the machine is used bilaterally.* Asymmetrical stress in the leg press is best avoided, because it increases the risk of injury.

Hammer Strength Iso-Lateral Leg Press, used unilaterally. This is risky. Instead, train both legs simultaneously.

Because the unilateral leg press can be used bilaterally, be conservative and use it in bilateral mode only.

The leg press produces compression of the lower back. If you start with minimal weight, use correct technique, smooth rep speed, and build up resistance gradually, your body should adapt to the compression, be strengthened by it, and may suffer no negative consequences. Some trainees, however, will be unable to leg press safely because of the compression.

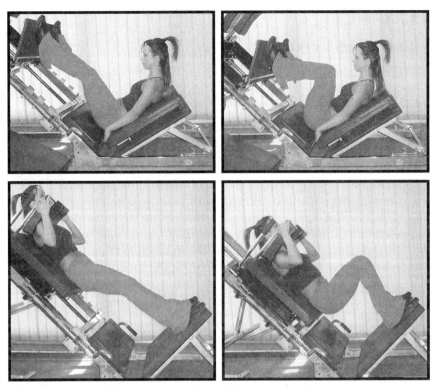

Some leg press machines have constructional problems. The foot plate of the one illustrated in the top photographs, for example, isn't big enough, which precludes correct foot positioning, especially for larger trainees. And the hand supports aren't positioned well. Because the model shown here is diminutive, the shortcomings of this machine aren't as pronounced as they would be for a large trainee.

This leg press doubles as a hack squat machine—see above photographs. Modern hack squat machines are more like reverse leg presses than machine versions of the barbell hack squat. The latter is an awkward exercise. Machine designers have tried to improve the hack squat.

The variety of hack squat machines is considerable, and the quality varies across the brands. There's a variety of leg press machines, too, but the extent of variation isn't so extensive, and most public gyms have a decent leg press.

Hack squat machines aren't recommended in this book because of the extent of their variation. If used properly—correct foot positioning (like in the barbell squat), concave lower spine, safe range of motion, controlled rep speed, and gradual building up of resistance—some of these machines are good. But some of them are constructed in such a way that they will harm most users if used regularly.

13. L-FLY

Main muscles worked

infraspinatus, teres minor

Capsule description

with a bent, fixed elbow, move its hand outward against resistance

This is an important exercise because it strengthens two commonly neglected articular muscles of the shoulder: infraspinatus, and teres minor, both of which rotate the humerus *externally*, or laterally, and also adduct it. The other two articular muscles are the subscapularis, which rotates the humerus *internally*, or medially; and the supraspinatus, which abducts the humerus only. The tendons of these four muscles fuse with tissues of the shoulder joint, at the rotator cuff.

The L-fly acts to reduce the strength imbalance between the external (weaker) and internal (stronger) rotator muscles of the shoulder. The internal rotators include the powerful pecs and lats. An excessive strength imbalance between the opposing external and internal rotators is a major contributing factor to shoulder problems.

To distinguish between the external and internal rotators of your humerus, imagine you're shaking someone's hand with your right hand. Keep your right elbow bent at a right angle, and your elbow fixed at your side. Moving your right hand to the right is *external* rotation, while moving your right hand to the left is *internal* rotation.

The L-fly has a small weight potential. A male novice may need a year or more to build up to using just ten pounds, and a female novice may need a year or more to build up to using just four or five pounds.

The use of small discs is critical, to ensure that progressive resistance is applied *gradually*.

Performance

Lie on your left side on a bench, and place your left hand on the floor, for stability. With a small plate or very light dumbbell in your right hand, form a 90-degree angle at your elbow—the L shape. Put your right elbow on your right oblique muscles, or hip, depending on your body structure. A folded towel placed in the hollow between your hip and rib cage may help you to maintain the correct elbow positioning. Lower the weight until your right forearm rests against your abs, then raise your right forearm as far as possible. Keep your right elbow fixed

Lying L-fly. Lift your forearm as near to vertical as possible.

against your side throughout the set. Inhale on the descent, and exhale on the ascent. Finish the set, turn around, then work your left side.

Do the exercise slowly—three seconds for the lifting phase, a pause for a second at the top, a further three seconds for the lowering phase, a pause for a second at the bottom, then smoothly move into the next ascent.

Never train the L-fly to failure, never raise your elbow, and never roll backward even a little.

Variations

The L-fly can be performed while standing, using a cable or band that runs horizontally to the floor at about waist height. Stand sideways to the cable, right foot nearest the cable, your feet about hip-width apart, a single cable handle in your left hand, left elbow near your left side and bent at a right angle, and left forearm across your abdomen. Rest your right hand on your right hip or thigh. That's the starting position. Slowly and smoothly move your left hand outward. Keep your left humerus vertical, left elbow near your left side, and left forearm parallel with the floor. Pause for a second at the point of fullest rotation, and smoothly and slowly return to the starting position. Pause for a second, then repeat.

Alternatively, use the cable from a floor pulley. Kneel on your heels on the floor, sideways to the pulley, and the midpoint of your thighs in line with the pulley. Space your knees for stability, keep your torso vertical, and perform the L-fly as described for the standing cable version. You may, however, need to keep the elbow of your working arm a little further away from your body, for better alignment with

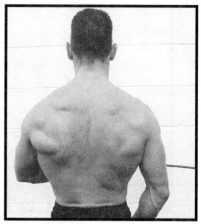

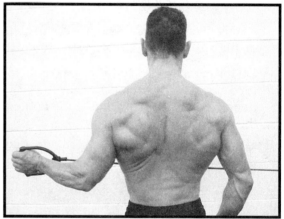

Cable L-fly, standing.

the direction of the cable, because the cable may not be horizontal to the floor, depending on the apparatus, and your size. Set your elbow position for the cable pathway that feels the most comfortable, and keep it fixed there throughout the set.

Take special care with any variation of the cable or pulley L-fly. The muscular tension arising from these forms of the L-fly is such that when your muscles tire, near the end of a set, it's especially easy to lose the groove of a rep, and get injured. The dumbbell lying L-fly can be controlled better, and is safer.

Furthermore, depending on the minimum resistance of the cable or pulley arrangement, you may first need to build sufficient strength by using the lying L-fly, which can start from a tiny plate or other item. And incremental resistance isn't possible with the type of cables that come in bands—to progress from one band to two, for example, is a huge jump. Incremental resistance *can* be applied to the lying L-fly, and the pulley L-fly.

Pulley L-fly, kneeling. If, when the pulley is lined up with the midpoint of your thighs, the resistance is too great at the minimum setting, you may be able to reduce it if you sit further back, depending on the design of the apparatus. If so, then as your strength increases, gradually move forward until the midpoint of your thighs is lined up with the pulley. Then increase the resistance with a tiny increment.

The L-fly acts to reduce the strength imbalance between the external (weaker) and internal (stronger) rotator muscles of the shoulders. An excessive strength imbalance between these opposing muscles is a major contributing factor to shoulder problems.

14. NECK WORK

Main muscles worked

sternocleidomastoid, upper trapezius
deeper muscles, over and between the cervical vertebrae, are also involved

Capsule description

seated or lying, move your head against resistance

The neck may be the most responsive bodypart, probably because it receives so little exercise during the course of regular living. Neck work must, however, be done with special care, because the neck is easily injured. As well as improving your physique, neck work—when done correctly—will increase your resistance to neck injuries from training, accidents, and during sleep.

There are six functions of the neck: extension (to the rear), forward flexion, flexion to the right, flexion to the left, rotation to the right, and rotation to the left. The entire musculature of the neck is worked through extension and forward flexion alone—the upper trapezius through extension, and the sternocleidomastoid through forward flexion. These two movements are also perhaps the simplest neck exercises, and the only ones recommended in this book. Lateral flexion, and rotation, may also carry a greater risk of injury than extension, and forward flexion.

Neck caution

In all neck work—non-machine, and machine—the speed of movement must be smooth and slow at all times, including the turnaround points of each rep. Keep the rep speed no faster than four seconds for each phase, plus a pause for a second at the position of fullest contraction, and another second in the starting position, for at least ten seconds total per rep.

Manual resistance neck work

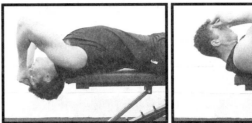

For forward flexion, lie on your back on a bench, with your head and neck off the end. Don't extend your head in an exaggerated way. Extend only to a degree that feels comfortable. Place your fingers on your forehead and gently push down for resistance. Slowly raise and lower your head, and apply manual resistance during both phases of each rep.

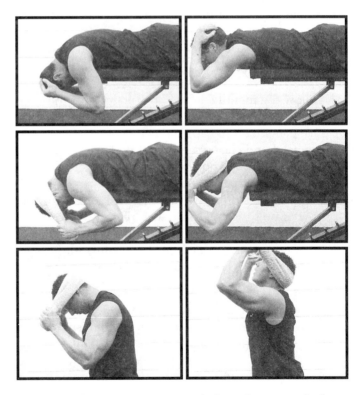

For extension against resistance, turn around, face down, and place your hands on the rear of your head. Alternatively, apply resistance using a small towel held between your hands and across the rear of your head. Slowly raise and lower your head, and apply manual resistance during both phases of each rep. The extension can also be done seated.

Before doing the work sets of extension, or flexion, perform a warm-up set without any manual resistance. For the work sets, after an introductory period of several weeks of progressive adaptation from a very easy start, apply enough resistance to make each rep taxing.

Don't use an exaggerated range of motion, *always* use a *slow* rep speed, and *never* use jerky movements. Do each rep *smoothly,* and use resistance that permits moderate to high reps—consider 10 reps as the minimum.

Four-way neck machine

A four-way neck machine is the first choice for neck work. Used correctly, it provides comfortable, controlled, direct, full-range, and safe exercise with measurable, incremental resistance. Manual resistance doesn't permit measurable, progressive resistance.

Forward flexion

Follow the manufacturer's instructions for the correct set-up position. The force against the face pad should be applied evenly over your forehead and cheek bones, and perhaps upper jaw, too, but not your lower jaw. And there should be no pressure on your eyes. Grip the handles just sufficiently to hold position. Using little or no resistance, fine-tune the set-up until you find what works best for you—this may take several workouts. Make a note in your training log of the pin position(s) for the set-up.

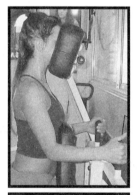

Move as far forward as is comfortable—ideally to the point where your chin touches your upper chest. If the full range of motion isn't comfortable initially, it may become so after a few workouts. Only your head and neck move—there should be no movement of your torso. Don't pull with your hands to help complete the neck flexion. Hold the position of full forward flexion for a second.

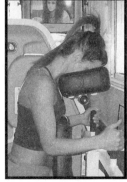

On the return to the starting position, never go beyond the vertical-neck, starting position; and *ease* into the starting position. A loss of control, and thrusting into the starting position, will jar your neck and may lead to a whiplash-like effect, and injury.

Following completion of the final rep, exit the machine with control so that you avoid jolting—don't suddenly unload your neck.

Extension

Follow the manufacturer's instructions for the correct set-up position. You'll probably need a seat position two to four inches *lower* for neck extension than what you use for forward flexion. Keep your back against the bench, and start each rep from where your chin touches your chest (ideally), or from where it's near your chest, according to comfort. If you have to lean forward, or slouch, to adopt the correct starting position, you have the seat positioned too high. Keep your chest high, not sunken or deflated—don't slump—to avoid excessive forward range of motion. Position the head pad so that it doesn't move during the exercise. If the full range of motion isn't comfortable initially, it may become so after a few workouts. Grip the handles just sufficiently to hold position. Place your feet out in front, with your knees only slightly bent, to brace yourself. Then you may not need to hold the handles. Instead, keep your hands on your chest, and exercise your neck without any assistance from your hands.

Using little or no resistance, fine-tune the set-up until you find what works best for you. It may take several workouts before you find the set-up that suits you best. Make a note in your training log of the pin position(s) for the set-up.

Extend your head—move it rearward—while maintaining a fixed torso. Only move your head and neck. Extend as far as is comfortable—don't force an exaggerated range of motion. And don't push with your hands to help complete the neck extension. Pause for a second in the position of full extension, then smoothly and slowly return to the starting position while keeping your chest in a fixed, high position. Pause for a second, then move into the next rep.

Following completion of the final rep, with your chin on or near your chest, under perfect control, exit the machine without jolting your neck.

15. PARALLEL BAR DIP

Main muscles worked

pectorals, triceps, deltoids, latissimus dorsi

Capsule description

while on parallel bars, lower and raise yourself through bending at your elbows

Most trainees can dip safely *if* they use correct, controlled technique. If you've had shoulder problems in the past, and the dip bothers you no matter how careful you are, you may still be able to use the machine version safely.

Men who have the most difficulty with dips are frequently heavy. Other factors that lead to difficulty with dips are rounded shoulders, and shortened pectoral muscles. If you're tight in those areas, work for a few weeks on gradually increasing your shoulder and pectoral flexibility before you start dipping.

Female beginners usually have difficulty with the dip, but can prosper on the machine version. The orthodox dip has bodyweight as the minimum resistance; but with the machine dip, resistance starts from almost nothing.

Set-up

If there are multiple pairs of parallel bars, or an adjustable pair, try various width positions. About 22 inches or 56 centimeters between the centers of the bars is a good starting point for most men. Women and slender or small men will be more comfortable with closer bars. Big men may prefer wider bars. Try v-shaped bars to find the optimum hand spacing for you. Face the part of the unit where the v-shaped bars come together, not where they fan out. Another option is to use a power rack. If its uprights are suitably spaced, position a bar on saddles on the front uprights, and another bar on the rear uprights. Set the height of the bars at what's ideal for you.

Some v-shaped bars have thick handles, which enable the load to be spread over a bigger area of the hands, and produce greater comfort than regular-thickness bars. The thick handles also permit fine-tuning of hand positioning, for greater comfort.

Regardless of the type of set-up, the bars must be securely fixed so that they can't wobble as you dip.

Three set-ups for the parallel bar dip: unit with V-shaped bars (left), standing machine, seated machine.

Positioning

Find the strongest, most comfortable, and natural dipping position for you. Distribute the stress from the dip over all the involved muscles. Don't try to focus the stress on any one particular area.

Stand on a box or bench of the right height so that you can easily get into the elbows-locked-out position. When you bend your knees and descend into the dip, your tibias just below your kneecaps should graze the box or bench when you're at your maximum safe depth. For most trainees, this is where the rear arm is parallel with the floor, or a little beneath that point. Some trainees can safely dip below the parallel position, whereas others need to stop a little above parallel.

To find a depth marker to suit you, try various benches or boxes. To fine-tune, place something of the correct thickness on top of the best-fit bench or box, preferably something with a soft surface.

Dipping so that your tibias graze something at your maximum safe depth isn't just to prevent overstretching. It ensures accurate record keeping. Without a marker to ensure consistent rep depth, there's a tendency to shorten the reps at the end of a set.

Performance

Never bounce (or *pre-stretch* as it's sometimes called) at the bottom of the dip, and avoid doing reps rapidly. Go down slowly, pause for a second at the bottom, and push up in a controlled, smooth manner. Never relax at the bottom.

Keep your elbows in the same plane as your wrists, or slightly to the outside of that plane. Take a pause for a second between reps at the top position, but don't let your shoulders slump as you hold yourself on locked elbows. Keep your head and shoulders up high, and stay tight. Women in particular may find it uncomfortable to lock out fully. In such cases, stop the ascent just short of the fully locked out position.

Don't let your lower limbs swing as you dip, and neither thrust your head forward nor throw it back. Furthermore, keep your chest stuck out to help keep your shoulders pulled back and safe.

Never descend on a deflated chest. Inhale before you descend, then exhale during the ascent. Going into the bottom position of the dip on a deflated chest increases the risk of injury, so keep your chest full during the descent and early part of the ascent.

Other tips

To warm up for the dip, start with floor push-ups. Then from the upright position of the dip, perform partial reps as you gradually work into your bottom position. Then you would be ready for a work set. If you use a dip machine, matters are simpler, because you have full control over resistance.

For the non-machine dip, find a method of attaching weights comfortably and securely. Use of a purpose-made weight belt for the parallel bar dip is the most common option. An alternative, at least for attaching small weights, is to wear any strong, leather belt normally used for trousers, and put a dumbbell inside it through having the 'bell vertical and the belt across the handle. Another option is to use a piece of strong rope to attach a dumbbell or plates to your belt. Let the resistance hang at the front of your thighs. If that's uncomfortable, try suspending it from the rear. The resistance must not hang so low that it touches your depth marker before you reach your bottom position.

Strength permitting, add weight slowly and in small increments. To work from one fixed-weight dumbbell to the next, attach one or more small discs, or use an adjustable dumbbell. Alternatively, use individual weight plates, with a belt fitted through them before being buckled.

With the machine dip, a slight change in torso or wrist position can produce significant improvement in comfort, and the range of movement can be easily controlled. In addition, because resistance starts at little or nothing, the machine unit can be used by trainees who don't yet have the strength to do regular parallel bar dips.

Spotting

The main markers of technique deterioration are swinging lower limbs, throwing the head back, back arching, elbows wobbling, and stalling. The spotter should stand behind you. If you dip on bars attached to a wall, dip facing the wall so that your spotter has plenty of room. The spotter should place his hands under your shins—with your knees bent—and apply the minimum of assistance that's necessary if you require help to complete a rep.

Purpose-made weight belt with attachments, for the parallel bar dip.

A shoulder harness isn't illustrated, but is the preferred option—for safety, and comfort—if a substantial poundage is to be attached to a suspended body. A substantial poundage attached around the waist or hips may apply an unsafe load on the spine during the parallel bar dip because the body is suspended and the forces pulling on the vertebrae may be excessive.

16. PRESS

The overhead press is usually called the *press*, without the *overhead* qualifier. When done standing, it's called the *military press*. The press can be done seated, to reduce the tendency to lean back. It can also be done seated against a high-incline bench, to remove much of the stress from the lower back—this is the most conservative form of the press.

Seated barbell press

Main muscles worked

deltoids, triceps, trapezius

Capsule description

seated, push resistance from your shoulders to overhead

Set-up

Don't use a vertical bench. Use one set at about 75 to 80 degrees. Tilt the seat a little, if it's adjustable, to help prevent your slipping off the bench while pressing. Ensure any adjustable bench you use is sturdy, heavy, and stable.

Many gyms have purpose-built units for the seated barbell press, with fixed back support, and built-in uprights to hold the bar. Some can be good, but most have problems. The back support may be too upright, or too tall. Because the uprights that support the bar are usually behind the trainee, a spotter is essential for unracking and racking the bar. Taking the bar unassisted from behind your head is bad for your shoulders, and pressing from behind your neck can be harmful, too. The press behind neck is an unnatural movement that causes neck, shoulder, and rotator cuff problems for many trainees, and is best avoided.

The seated press can be done in a power rack. Position the bench inside the rack so that you can't hit the uprights with the bar during a rep. Load the bar on pins set at the height from which you press.

You can also do the seated press close to squat stands. Position yourself and the stands so that you have minimum handling problems getting the barbell out of the stands to start a set, and returning it to the stands at the end of a set. Spotters should be used here so that you don't have to wrestle with the bar.

Don't use a machine that forces you to use a vertical bar pathway, such as a Smith machine. That will lock you into an unnatural groove that commonly leads to shoulder problems.

Positioning

When you're sat on the bench ready to press, your feet should be wider than shoulder width. Flare your feet for greater stability, and keep your heels directly beneath or slightly in front of an imaginary vertical line drawn through the middle of your knees.

The bottom position from where you press is typically at about the height of your clavicles (when you're in your pressing position), or a little higher (at, or just below chin height). For shoulder comfort, long-limbed trainees will need a slightly higher starting position than will short-limbed trainees. Starting too low will put excessive stress on the shoulder joints.

Take a pronated grip on the barbell. Start with a hand spacing two inches wider on each side than your shoulder width, and fine-tune from there. Don't use a thumbless grip. Your forearms should be vertical at the bottom position of the press, when viewed from the front or rear.

Note the two flaws in this starting position for the seated press from the pins of a power rack. The elbows need to be moved forward to produce forearms nearer to vertical. And the lower back shows exaggerated arching, largely because the heels are behind the knees.

Performance

Push the bar up vertically, and keep the rest of your body braced. Don't let the bar move forward. Push it up near your face, but be careful not to strike your face. Apply force evenly with both arms and shoulders. Don't let one hand get ahead of or in front of the other. Once the bar is above your head, allow it to travel two to three inches to the rear as it ascends, for a more natural pathway than a perfectly vertical one. Lock out your elbows smoothly, without jolting. Pause for a second at the top position.

Lower the bar under control, don't lower it beyond your safe point, and don't bounce at the bottom. Pause momentarily at the bottom before pushing the bar up, but don't relax at the bottom. Keep yourself tight, like a coiled spring.

Inhale at the top during the brief pause, or during the descent; and exhale during the ascent.

Keep a rigid wrist position during the press. Don't allow the weight to bend your hands backward more than just a little, because that can mar your lifting technique, and injure your wrists, too. Grip the bar firmly, to help keep your wrists in the right position.

Keep all your body's musculature tensed as you press and lower the bar, especially your legs, thighs, abdominals, buttocks, and back.

Back support height

If the back support from the bench is too tall, it won't allow your head to go back a little, out of the way of the barbell's ideal pathway. This would put the bar forward of the ideal pathway—to prevent striking your face—mar the exercise, and could produce injury because of poor distribution of stress. A shortened back support would be required. Alternatively, use dumbbells.

Spotting

At the end of a set of the press, the groove can easily be lost. The spotter should look out for the barbell tipping, one hand getting forward of the other, or the bar being pressed off center. The moment that one of those markers occurs, the spotter should provide assistance to prevent more serious technique deterioration.

The spotter should stand as close as possible behind the presser, to be able to apply assistance easily. The spotter must use both hands, apply help in a balanced way, and maintain a slightly arched back.

Caution

To help prevent back injuries while pressing, preserve a non-exaggerated hollow in your lower back. This is the natural weight-bearing formation.

To avoid exaggerating the hollow in your lower back while performing the seated press, keep your feet flat on the floor, with your heels directly beneath your knees, or a little in front of them.

> *The press behind neck is an unnatural movement that causes neck, shoulder, and rotator cuff problems for many trainees, and is best avoided. The press from the* FRONT *is safer. If you find the barbell press awkward, use the dumbbell press instead.*

Seated dumbbell press

Main muscles worked

deltoids, triceps, trapezius

Capsule description

seated, push resistance from your shoulders to overhead

Dumbbell pressing can be done simultaneously, or by alternating hands. For the alternating dumbbell press, press with one hand as you lower with the other, or press and lower one dumbbell while the other waits at its shoulder. This produces asymmetrical stress and encourages leaning from side to side. Simultaneous pressing is safer.

Getting dumbbells into position

Set up a bench with an incline of 75 to 80 degrees, and tilt its seat if it's adjustable. Then get the help of an assistant or, better yet, two assistants to hand you the dumbbells, or use the following method.

Stand immediately in front of a bench, feet about hip-width apart. Each dumbbell should touch the outside of its corresponding foot, with the two handles parallel with each other. Bend your knees and take the 'bells from the floor with a parallel grip and correct deadlifting technique. Because of the small-diameter plates on the dumbbells, the range of motion when lifting them from the floor is considerable. Taking the 'bells from off a rack or boxes is safer than lifting them directly off the floor, provided that good lifting technique is used.

While standing, center the rear end of each dumbbell on its corresponding thigh just above the knee. If you use dumbbells with protruding ends or collars—probably adjustable 'bells—place just the inside part of the bottom plate of a given dumbbell on the outside of its corresponding lower thigh. This will work if the radius of the dumbbell plate concerned is sufficient so that you can have the 'bell positioned vertically on your thigh while you're seated. The collars must be securely in place—a 'bell that falls apart during use could be disastrous.

Keep the dumbbells against your thighs, and sit on the bench, with your hips against the bottom of the back support. The 'bells will move into a vertical position as you sit down. The dumbbells must remain against your thighs, just above your knees.

Clockwise, from the bottom left, how to get into position for the seated dumbbell press without assistance, and the first ascent of the set.

Once you're sat on the bench, pause for a moment and then thrust your left knee up and simultaneously pull vigorously with your left arm. This will get the dumbbell to your left shoulder. Do the same for your right side.

Once you have the dumbbells at your shoulders, *roll* your back onto the back support—don't keep an arched back as you lean backward. Now, you'll be in position for pressing, with your back supported.

When you've finished a set of dumbbell presses, move your feet and knees together, and lower the 'bells directly to the floor, quickly but under control. Keep the dumbbells well away from your legs and thighs. Alternatively, return the 'bells to your thighs using a reverse of the handling that got them to your shoulders. Control the dumbbells—don't let them crash onto your thighs. Then stand and return the dumbbells to their rack.

Before you do any dumbbell pressing, practice handling the 'bells.

The use of competent spotters will resolve the handling issue.

Performance

The dumbbell press allows you to find the wrist positioning and pressing groove that feel most comfortable for you. Your hands can be parallel with each other, pronated, or somewhere in between. Try each variation, and find the dumbbell pathway that feels the strongest and most comfortable for you. For example, start with your hands parallel with each other at shoulder height and, during the top half of the movement, move your hands to or toward a pronated position.

Keep a rigid wrist position, and don't allow the weights to bend your hands backward more than just a little, because that can mar your lifting technique, and injure your wrists, too.

By permitting the natural positioning of your hands at the sides of your head, your head doesn't get in the way, unlike with a barbell.

Keep the dumbbells directly over your shoulders. Don't let them drift out to the sides, and don't overstretch at the bottom.

Push up smoothly from the bottom position, pause for a second at the top position, lower under control, pause momentarily at the bottom while keeping your entire body tight and tensed, then push smoothly into the next rep.

Pressing from a parallel grip at the bottom, to a pronated one at the top.

Spotting

Spotting someone who's pressing dumbbells can be awkward. One hand should apply force under each elbow. This is strictly for assisting the trainee to get a tough rep up in correct technique. A single person can't simultaneously take a pair of dumbbells from a presser who fails on a rep—two spotters are needed. With dumbbell pressing, the key markers of technique regression to look out for are the 'bells drifting out to the sides, and one hand getting above, in front of, or to the rear of the other.

Caution

To help prevent back injuries while pressing, preserve a non-exaggerated hollow in your lower back. This is the natural weight-bearing formation.

To avoid exaggerating the hollow in your lower back while performing the seated dumbbell press, keep your feet flat on the floor, with your heels directly beneath your knees, or a little in front of them. If your feet are behind your knees, the arch will probably be exaggerated, and the risk of injury increased.

17. PULLDOWN

Main muscles worked

latissimus dorsi, upper back, pectorals, biceps, brachialis, forearms

Capsule description

sit beneath an overhead pulley, pull the bar to your chest

Set-up

Sit in the pulldown apparatus so that the cable runs vertically during the exercise, or sloped slightly toward you. A common mistake is to sit too far in the apparatus. Brace your thighs under the T-shaped restraint that has been set at the correct height for you.

Grip

There are several bar and grip options. Use the one that lets you use the most resistance over the fullest but safe range of motion.

With a straight bar, start with a supinated and shoulder-width grip, and fine-tune your hand spacing for wrist and elbow comfort. A hand spacing a little closer than shoulder-width may work best for the supinated grip.

For the parallel grip, a shoulder-width spacing produces a better effect than a close grip. Grip each handle in the center.

For the parallel and supinated grips, use a hand spacing that keeps your forearms vertical during the exercise, provided that's safe for you.

The parallel grip results in a smaller weight potential than a supinated grip. Comparing the same range of motion, you'll need about 15% less weight with a parallel grip than a supinated one.

If a supinated grip is uncomfortable, even after having tried different hand spacings, and the bar for a shoulder-width, parallel grip is unavailable, try a pronated grip using a straight bar. Take it two to three inches wider on each side than your shoulder-width grip, so that your forearms are vertical at the contracted position of the exercise.

Regardless of the bar you choose, avoid a wide grip, and don't pull to the rear of your head. Pulling to the rear is an unnatural action that puts unnecessary stress on the neck, cervical vertebrae, and shoulders.

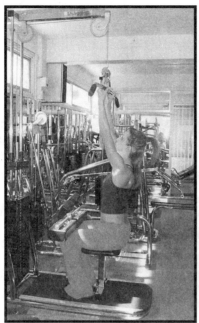

Correct top and bottom positions of the pulldown, using a supinated grip.

Pulling to the rear doesn't improve the muscle- and strength-building values of the pulldown, but increases the risk of injury.

Performance

Look forward or upward, and smoothly pull the bar until your hands are at your upper chest or a little lower, according to wrist and shoulder comfort.

During the descent, lean back only a little and arch your back slightly. Never round your back. If you have to round your back or crunch your abdominal muscles to help, the weight is too heavy. If you round your shoulders, you'll be unable to pull your shoulder blades down, and will rob yourself of working the target musculature properly.

If you can't pull your hands to below your clavicles, the weight is too heavy and you'll be unable to pull your shoulder blades down fully. Make a special effort to pull your shoulder blades down, but don't pull beyond what feels comfortable for your shoulders and elbows.

Pause for a second in the contracted position (at your chest), then let your elbows straighten smoothly and under control. The weight stack must not yank on any structure. Keep your shoulders tight when

Common errors in the pulldown.

your arms are extended. Never relax in order to get extra stretch. Pause for a second at the top, then smoothly move into the next rep.

Look forward or slightly upward at all times, and keep your head in a neutral position—don't turn, crane, or extend your head. Exhale as you pull the bar down, and inhale as you straighten your elbows.

Use chalk or rosin on your hands when you need grip support. If the bar is smooth, the chalk or rosin won't help you as much as they will with a bar that has knurling. To help your grip on a slick bar, put a palm-size piece of neoprene between each hand and the bar. Neoprene is a synthetic rubber with many uses. Get some small pieces from a scuba gear shop, an engineering storeroom on campus, or a hardware store.

Spotting

Spotting isn't essential here, because the weight can't come down on you. But spotting is desirable for ensuring that the final rep of a demanding set is done correctly. Technique starts to become ragged when your shoulders start to round. A spotter can push on the bar or pull on the weight stack.

Adding weight

Selectorized cable units, and selectorized machines in general, commonly have weight increments of 10 pounds or 5 kilos, and larger in some cases. This is too much weight to progress by in a single jump. Where you train may have special weights of 5 pounds or 2.5 kilos—and perhaps smaller ones, too—designed to fit on the top of a weight stack. If it doesn't, you may be able to get your own from an exercise equipment store. Use them to help you to work from one pin setting to the next.

Alternatively, place the weight selection pin through a small barbell weight plate before the pin goes into the weight stack. Although a pin that holds a plate won't go fully into the weight stack, it should go through enough to hold the plate securely and select the resistance, too.

Magnetic small plates are another option for adding small increments of weight to a stack.

Whichever option you choose, check that the set-up is secure before you perform a set.

> For the pulldown, regardless of the bar you choose, avoid a wide grip, and don't pull to the rear of your head. Pulling to the rear is an unnatural action that puts unnecessary stress on the neck, cervical vertebrae, and shoulders. Pulling to the rear doesn't improve the muscle- and strength-building values of the pulldown, but increases the risk of injury.

18. PULLOVER

There are two types of pullover—the muscle-building one that requires a machine, and the type that may have potential for enlarging the rib cage. Both involve moving resistance from behind your head. The former has your elbows bent, whereas the other keeps your elbows straight or almost straight.

Machine pullover

Main muscles worked

latissimus dorsi, pectorals, triceps, abdominal wall

Capsule description

move resistance from behind your head, with bent elbows

Use a machine, not a barbell, single dumbbell, or pair of dumbbells. Some pullover machines are better than others. If you find a machine that suits you, exploit it. It will enable you to train your lats without your elbow flexors, and grip, limiting you. Most other exercises for the lats require substantial involvement of the elbow flexors, and grip.

Some pullover machines have the user apply force through the elbows or rear arms, which are positioned against pads. Other machines require the user to apply force solely against a bar that's held by the hands. The former is the pick of the two machines. If only the other type is available, use the pulldown, chin-up, or pull-up instead.

Some pullover machines, like the one shown in the photographs, have pads for the arms and a bar for the hands. Here, focus on applying force through the arms against the pads.

Set-up and positioning

Find the best set-up for you according to your torso and arm lengths. Follow the manufacturer's set-up guidance, and fine-tune the adjustments to find the body and arm positioning that enables you to work hard without producing any joint soreness. Depending on the machine, you may have to adjust the height of the seat, and the range-of-motion limiter. The machine must have a belt, to restrain your pelvis.

Your shoulder joints should line up with the pivot points of the machine, or perhaps be an inch or so below the pivot points. Sit with your hips and back firmly against the back support, and have an assistant view the pivot points from the height of your shoulders, to determine the correct positioning. Move the seat height accordingly.

Some pullover machines have a foot pedal or bar that's used to assist with proper set-up, and to transfer the resistance to and from the user. Once the resistance has been selected, and the trainee is seated and belted into position, the pedal must be depressed so that the elbows can be positioned on the pads of the movement arm. Removing the feet from the pedal transfers the resistance to the trainee, for the first rep. After the set is finished, the foot pedal is depressed again, to unload the resistance so that the elbows can be removed from the movement arm.

The danger in the pullover primarily comes from an excessive range of motion for the shoulders in the top, stretched position. Set the seat at the right height for you, push your hips as far back on the seat as possible, and strap yourself in tightly. Then with a very light weight on the machine, discover how far back you can take your arms before your back starts to come off the back support. Your starting position should be about an inch short of the point where your back starts to come off the back support. Set up the machine accordingly. Then keep your back against the machine's back support.

If even this less-than-full-range of motion irritates your shoulders, reduce it until there's no irritation. Over the first few weeks of use, however, your shoulder flexibility may increase, and thus you may be able to increase your range of motion a little.

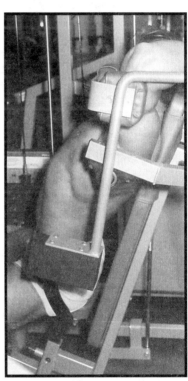

A dangerous starting position for the pullover. Note the exaggerated arch in the lower back.

If the machine you use doesn't have a built-in range-of-motion control to delimit the top, stretched position, you can do it manually if it has a weight stack. See *Leg curl* for details.

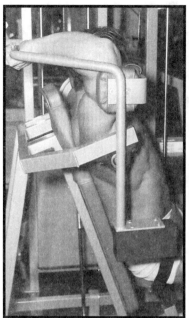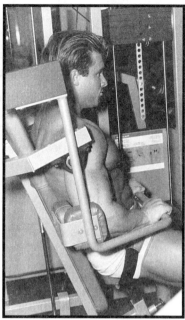

A reduced and safer range of motion in the machine pullover.

Over the first few times you use the pullover, you may need to fine-tune the set-up to find the one that feels the most comfortable for you.

Make a note in your training log of the settings you use.

Performance

Focus the exercise on your back musculature, not your arms. Mentally connect with your back musculature and direct the work there, consciously maximizing the contraction and involvement of your back.

Move out of the stretched position slowly. Move smoothly and under control at all times. Allow (but don't force) your neck to flex as you move into the contracted position. Keep your back against the back support throughout each rep. Only lightly hold the bar or handles with your hands. Focus on trying to crush the pads with your arms. Hold the fully contracted, bottom position for a second, and contract your lats hard.

As you return to the stretched, starting position, slow down. Pause in the starting position for a second, then smoothly move into the next rep. To protect your shoulders, don't relax them in the stretched, starting position. Keep your shoulders tensed.

This exercise has a large range of motion. You should take three to four seconds for each phase, plus the additional second for the hold in the contracted position, and another second for the pause at the starting position. Inhale as your arms move back, and exhale during the positive (or contraction) phase.

Although not essential, use a spotter once you're training hard. As soon as a rep grinds to a halt, the spotter should apply a tad of help. This will keep the rep moving, and help ensure correct technique.

Adding weight

Selectorized cable units, and selectorized machines in general, commonly have weight increments of 10 pounds or 5 kilos, and larger in some cases. This is too much weight to progress by in a single jump. Where you train may have special weights of 5 pounds or 2.5 kilos—and perhaps smaller ones, too—designed to fit on the top of a weight stack. If it doesn't, you may be able to get your own from an exercise equipment store. Use them to help you to work from one pin setting to the next.

Alternatively, place the weight selection pin through a small barbell weight plate before the pin goes into the weight stack. Although a pin that holds a plate won't go fully into the weight stack, it should go through enough to hold the plate securely and select the resistance, too.

Magnetic small plates are another option for adding small increments of weight to a stack.

Whichever option you choose, check that the set-up is secure before you perform a set.

Books on strength training and bodybuilding usually provide skimpy descriptions of exercise technique. But exercise technique isn't a simple matter. The exercises need to be described in detail. Please take the time to study the exercise descriptions. In order to train safely and effectively, it's critical that you MASTER exercise technique.

Breathing pullover

Main structure worked

rib cage

Capsule description

move resistance to and from behind your head, with straight elbows

This is a stretching and forced breathing exercise that may enlarge your rib cage, deepen your chest, and help to improve your posture. It may be especially effective for teenagers, and trainees in their early twenties, but is worth a try at any age. There's no science to confirm this, however. I believe the breathing pullover helped me, and other people have reported benefits, too.

Use no more than 10 pounds to begin with—a short and unloaded bar, a pair of small dumbbells, a single dumbbell, or a barbell plate. (The pullover machine shouldn't be used for the breathing pullover.) After a few months you may increase to 15 pounds, and later on to 20 pounds if you're a large man, but no more. Don't use progressive resistance in this exercise. The use of heavy weights will defeat the purpose of the exercise, as well as risk harm to your shoulders. If in doubt over which weight to use here, select the lighter one.

Hold the resistance and lie lengthwise on a bench, not across it. Keep your feet on the bench. This will prevent excessive arching of your back, and excessive stretching of your abdominal wall. Hold the resistance above your upper chest, with straight elbows. Take a shoulder-width grip, or closer if you're using a single dumbbell, or weight plate. Keep your elbows stiff and straight throughout, slowly lower the bar and simultaneously inhale as deeply as possible. Don't inhale in one gulp, but in a steady stream. Spread your ribs as much as possible. Lower your arms until they are parallel or only slightly below parallel with the floor. Don't go down as deep as possible. At the bottom position, take an extra gulp of air. Pause for a second, then return to the starting position, simultaneously exhaling. Repeat for at least 15 slow reps. Focus on stretching your rib cage.

Experiment with a different positioning. Do the exercise with your head just off the end of the bench, as illustrated. This may produce a better effect on your rib cage.

Keeping your elbows completely straight may irritate them. If so, bend your elbows slightly. Keep this to the minimum, however, or you'll reduce the potential expansion effect on your rib cage.

Elbow irritation may come from using more weight than has been recommended, or from not introducing the exercise into your program carefully enough. Elbow irritation may also come from using a straight bar, whereas a parallel grip on a weight plate, or dumbbell(s), may be safe.

The breathing pullover is traditionally done immediately after an exercise that gets you heavily winded, such as the squat, especially when the latter's done for higher reps.

Go easy at the beginning. The forced and exaggerated breathing may make you feel dizzy unless you work into it progressively over a few weeks. Your chest may get sore, too, if you don't work into the exercise *gradually*.

The Rader chest pull is an alternative to the breathing pullover.

19. PUSHDOWN

Main muscles worked

triceps

Capsule description

using resistance from an overhead pulley, press down with fixed elbows

The pushdown is sometimes called the *pressdown*, and is a form of the *triceps extension*. If you can't do the parallel bar dip, include the pushdown in your program. The parallel bar dip provides a degree of triceps extension that the bench press, close-grip bench press, incline bench press, and overhead presses don't. The pushdown provides a similar degree of triceps extension to that of the parallel bar dip, but from a single-joint exercise.

Keep your hands parallel with each other. This removes stress from your wrists and focuses it on your triceps. This style also protects your elbows because it helps to prevent wrist extension. Keep your wrists stiff and immobile throughout—don't let them flex or extend.

Use of a special, purpose-made rope attachment connected to the cable will enable you to keep your hands parallel with each other. If that attachment isn't available, securely attach your own sturdy but flexible strap or rope to the cable's connection. A bathrobe's belt can work well if you put a knot at the bottom of each end to prevent your hands slipping.

Push down under control until your elbows are straight, hold the contraction for a second, let the bar back up under control, pause in the top position for a second, and repeat. Keep your wrists rigid, your elbows fixed at the sides of your ribs, and your torso and lower limbs rigid. Focus on elbow extension and flexion. Exhale as you push down, and inhale as you let the resistance return to its starting position.

Don't use a range of motion that causes your forearms and biceps to crush together in the top position. Stop the ascent of your hands just before your forearms and biceps meet. And don't relax at the top of the pushdown. Keep tight control.

A homemade attachment for the pushdown—a bathrobe belt threaded through a carabiner, and knotted at both ends.

20. ROTARY TORSO

Main muscles worked

most of the abdominal wall, especially the external and internal obliques, and the multifidii

Capsule description

with your feet and hips fixed, rotate your torso to one side, and then the other

Although not a commonly available machine, the rotary torso may be available where you train. As well as training most of the abdominal wall, the rotary torso works some of the small, intervertebral muscles, but it provides only secondary involvement of the quadratus lumborum. It's an alternative to the side bend if the latter can't be performed safely.

The rotary torso is commonly performed in a dangerous manner—with an excessive range of motion, and a rep speed that's too fast.

Follow the manufacturer's set-up guidelines, and fix the range of motion at what feels comfortable for you. After a few weeks your flexibility may improve, and then you may be able to increase your range of motion.

Smoothly move into each rep, take three to four second to rotate into the fully contracted position, hold it for a second, then smoothly return to the starting position over a further three to four seconds. Pause for a second, then repeat. Complete the set for one side, pause for a minute and set up the machine for the other side of your body, then complete the set for that side.

Starting (left) and finishing positions for rotation to the trainee's right on the rotary torso machine.

Reminder

Study this book to learn about correct exercise technique, and then apply it *consistently*. If, however, despite using *correct technique*, along with a *controlled* rep speed, *gradual* increases in progressive resistance, *abbreviated* training routines, and *adequate* recovery time between workouts, you *still* experience joint or soft tissue irritation from a given exercise, substitute it with a comparable exercise.

Apply the first imperative of exercise: "Do no harm."

21. ROW

Four rows will be described: one-arm dumbbell row, cable row, machine row, and the prone low-incline dumbbell row. There are other rows, including the barbell row, and the T-bar row, both of which are fraught with danger. They don't have the body supported, the lower back is excessively involved, it's difficult to keep the lower back hollowed and secure once the weight becomes substantial—just a slight slip in technique can produce lower-back injury—and the wrist positioning they impose isn't ideal.

One-arm dumbbell row

Main muscles worked

latissimus dorsi, upper back, biceps, brachialis, rear deltoid, forearms

Capsule description

with one hand braced on a bench, take a dumbbell and pull it to your obliques

Stand next to a bench (or something stable of a similar height), with a dumbbell on the floor at your left side. Bend over and brace your right hand on the bench. Your right knee should be bent and your right foot well ahead of your left. Alternatively, your right knee could be placed on the bench. Either way, your left knee should be almost straight, and your torso inclined somewhat, as illustrated. Keep your lower back slightly hollowed throughout the exercise.

With your left hand, grab the dumbbell from the floor, with the handle parallel with your spine. Keep your elbow in, and smoothly pull the dumbbell as high as possible at your left oblique, or hip (depending on your body structure, and what feels comfortable for you). Pull in an arc, not a straight line. Don't yank the dumbbell up, don't rotate about your spine, and don't twist your torso. Only move your hand, forearm, arm, and shoulder.

Hold the top position for a second, and crush your shoulder blades together. At the top position, your elbow should be several inches above the height of your spine.

On the descent, smoothly retrace the arc of the ascent. At the bottom, pause for a second without relaxing or putting the dumbbell on the floor, then smoothly move into the next rep. Your forearm should be vertical or almost-vertical throughout the exercise. Inhale during the descent or while your elbow is straight, and exhale on the ascent.

Top left, correct starting position. Top right, incorrect finish. Middle, correct technique. Above, alternative set-up using a low-incline bench—probably the pick of the three variations—and correct technique.

This method works your left side. To train your right side, reverse the procedure.

To reduce the size of the weight jumps between fixed-weight dumbbells, use the same approach described for the *Dumbbell bench press*. But in the dumbbell row, use of wrist weights (obtainable from a sporting goods store) may be a good option for progressively working from one fixed-weight 'bell to the next. The wrist weights shouldn't spoil your balance in the dumbbell row, unlike in pressing movements.

Cable row

Main muscles worked

latissimus dorsi, upper back, biceps, brachialis, rear deltoid, forearms

Capsule description

while seated, pull to your waist or lower chest a bar fixed to a cable running from a low pulley

Set-up and positioning

Use a shoulder-width supinated grip on a straight bar, a shoulder-width (or slightly wider) pronated grip on a straight bar or, better still, use a shoulder-width *parallel grip* on a special bar. One of the most common mistakes in this exercise is doing it with hands too close. A shoulder-width grip produces a better effect than a narrow grip, because it keeps the forearms parallel and in a more natural position.

For the parallel grip, encourage the management where you train to get a shoulder-width bar if it doesn't already have one. If you're unsuccessful, buy your own bar, or get one custom made and take it with you when you're scheduled to do this exercise. Aim for a grip spacing that keeps your forearms parallel with each other throughout the exercise. Grasp each handle in the center.

Sit on the floor, or on the built-in low seat, with your feet against the foot restraint. If where you train doesn't have a foot restraint, improvise so that you have a solid foot brace that lets you space your feet as required.

The starting position has you seated with your torso vertical, lower back slightly hollowed, elbows pulled out straight by the resistance, knees slightly bent. To get into that position, bend your knees sufficiently so that you can take the handle with your back in the correct starting position. Then maintain the correct back positioning and straighten your knees sufficiently so that you won't bang them with the bar during the exercise. Keep your knees bent to some degree, to help you maintain the right back positioning.

Some cable row set-ups have cables that are too short, and it's difficult to get into the starting position. There's even the risk of injury while getting into position. To correct this, add a piece of chain between the bar and the cable, so that the bar is precisely where you want it for the starting position.

If you use a selectorized pulldown apparatus, you may be able to set up the weight stack so that the bar is where you want it for the starting position. See *Leg curl* for how to use the weight stack selector pin as a delimiter. But for a large adjustment, extra chain between the bar and cable may be required.

The top two photographs show correct technique, using a pronated, shoulder-width grip on a straight bar. The next one shows incorrect technique— raised elbows, and rounded back—but using the especially recommended PARALLEL, shoulder-width grip. The right photograph shows improved technique, but there's still some rearward lean that should be avoided.

Performance

Smoothly pull the bar into your upper abdomen or lower chest, according to what feels most natural for you according to the lengths of your torso, forearms, and arms. Keep your forearms parallel with the floor, and don't let your elbows drift out to the sides. Your elbows should be equally spaced throughout each rep. Arch your back slightly as you crush your shoulder blades together, but don't lean back. Your elbows must not rise when you're in the contracted position—keep your forearms parallel with the floor. Hold the contraction for a second, then let the resistance pull your elbows straight in a controlled manner. Pause for a second in the starting position, don't relax your shoulders, then smoothly move into the next rep.

Keep your torso upright and rigid throughout each rep. Imagine that your torso is supported, and can't move.

Each phase of a rep should take two to three seconds, plus an additional second for holding the contracted position, and another second at the starting position.

Other tips

If you lean back beyond the vertical, at least with a demanding weight, you'll round your shoulders, be unable to crush your shoulder blades together, and rob yourself of working the target muscles.

Don't relax your shoulders between reps, to permit a full stretch. A full stretch puts great stress on the rotator cuff muscles at the back of your shoulders, and will set you up for an injury. Keep your shoulders tight.

Look forward or slightly upward at all times, and keep your head in a neutral position—don't turn, crane, or extend your head.

Use chalk or rosin on your hands when you need grip support. If the bar is smooth, the chalk or rosin won't help you as much as they will with a bar that has knurling. To help your grip on a slick bar, put a palm-size piece of neoprene between each hand and the bar. Neoprene is a synthetic rubber with many uses. Get some small pieces from a scuba gear shop, an engineering storeroom on campus, or a hardware store.

Spotting

Spotting isn't essential here, because the resistance can't come down on you. Technique becomes ragged when your shoulders start to

Close-parallel-grip bars are commonly used in the cable row, but such a grip is inferior to a shoulder-width one. A shoulder-width PARALLEL grip is the ideal. The bottommost photograph shows an adjustable, parallel-grip bar—a single-width grip won't suit all users.

Use a shoulder-width pronated grip, or a shoulder-width supinated grip, as the alternative to the ideal of the shoulder-width parallel grip. Try both, to find which feels the most comfortable.

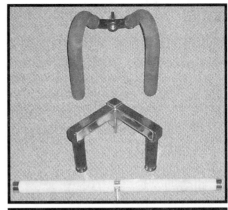

slump. Immediately, a spotter should pull on the weight stack cable just enough to enable you to get the rep out in correct technique.

Adding weight

Selectorized cable units, and selectorized machines in general, commonly have weight increments of 10 pounds or 5 kilos, and larger in some cases. This is too much weight to progress by in a single jump. Where you train may have special weights of 5 pounds or 2.5 kilos—and perhaps smaller ones, too—designed to fit on the top of a weight stack. If it doesn't, you may be able to get your own from an exercise equipment store. Use them to help you to work from one pin setting to the next.

Alternatively, place the weight selection pin through a small barbell weight plate before the pin goes into the weight stack. Although a pin that holds a plate won't go fully into the weight stack, it should go through enough to hold the plate securely and select the resistance, too.

Magnetic small plates are another option for adding small increments of weight to a stack.

Whichever option you choose, check that the set-up is secure before you perform a set.

Seated machine row

Main muscles worked

latissimus dorsi, upper back, biceps, brachialis, rear deltoid, forearms

Capsule description

sit and pull the handles to your waist or lower chest

This exercise is similar to the cable row, but with a simpler set-up. Furthermore, the chest is braced against a pad, which prevents the lower back from fatiguing, and thus increases stability and safety.

There may also be a foot bar, to help increase stability further. If there isn't, place your feet on the floor in front of you, wider than hip-width.

Depending on the machine, you may have the choice between a pronated grip, supinated grip, and a parallel grip. A parallel grip of shoulder-width is ideal.

If the parallel-grip handles are a lot closer than shoulder-width, use a pronated grip (palms down, in this case) of shoulder-width or a little wider, depending on comfort. A supinated grip (palms up, in this case) may feel comfortable, or it may irritate your wrists and elbows, depending on the positioning of the handles.

Adjust the seat's height to find the position that permits you to have your forearms parallel with the floor when you're in the contracted position. Pull your elbows as far behind you as possible, but keep your chest on the pad. Crush your shoulder blades together, hold the contraction, then let the resistance pull your elbows straight in a controlled manner. Pause in the starting position, don't relax your shoulders, then smoothly move into the next rep.

Keep your torso against the chest pad throughout each set, and your back slightly arched.

Take two to three seconds to pull the handles to your torso (the positive phase), pause for a second in the contracted position with your scapulae fully retracted, take two to three seconds for the negative phase, and a further second in the starting position.

Seated machine row.

Prone low-incline dumbbell row

This two-arm dumbbell
row is an alternative to
the one-arm variation
described earlier in this
section. It's also an
alternative to the cable
row, and the machine row.
Illustrated is the starting
position. You may need
to move your knees
further to the rear, so that
they aren't struck by the
dumbbells during the
ascent. Follow the same
pathway and control
guidelines as for the one-
arm dumbbell row.

22. SHRUG

Main muscles worked

trapezius, deltoids, forearms

Capsule description

while holding resistance, with straight elbows, shrug your shoulders

There are several types of shrugs, including upright, incline, and prone.

Set-up, and performance

Stand, with your elbows straight, and hold a bar as if you were in the top position of a deadlift. Without bending your elbows, smoothly shrug as high as possible—try to raise your shoulders to your ears—and pause for a second. Lower under control, pause for a second without relaxing, and repeat.

As an alternative to taking equipment from the floor for each set, place a barbell over pins set in a power rack at your bottom position, or, place a loaded barbell, parallel-grip bar, or dumbbells on boxes of the appropriate height. Position the dumbbells one at a time. You may need an assistant to help you set up the equipment.

Keep your body tight, a slight arch in your lower back (don't round your back), don't shuffle your feet around, and don't take more of the stress on one side of your body than the other. Keep the stress distributed symmetrically.

Dumbbells and a parallel-grip bar are ideal for the upright shrug. They aren't obstructed by your thighs or hips, unlike a straight bar. Use a parallel grip in the dumbbell shrug, with your hands by the sides of your thighs, or hips.

The barbell shrug and parallel-grip-bar shrug are performed standing only. The dumbbell shrug can be done seated, too, at the end of a bench.

Grip

Keep your elbows straight. Use your bench press grip or slightly wider. A close grip, or moving quickly, will prompt your elbows to bend. With a pronated grip, keep your elbows rotated inward, to lock your elbows.

Use a pronated grip on a straight bar with deep knurling, and chalk or rosin on your hands when you need grip support. Only when you

Three standing shrugs: barbell (left), dumbbell (middle), parallel-grip-bar (right). The parallel-grip-bar shrug illustrations show bending of the elbows. The elbows should be straight.

need further grip support should you use a reverse grip. From set to set, alternate which hand is supinated.

With a parallel-grip bar, or dumbbells, deep knurling is also required. Use chalk or rosin, too, when you need additional grip support.

Caution

Don't use a circular action when shrugging, because it places unnecessary wear on the shoulder joints. Furthermore, keep your shoulders tight at the bottom of each rep—don't let the weight yank your shoulders.

A common error is to stretch the head forward during the ascent. This can lead to neck and trapezius injuries. Keep your head in an upright, neutral position.

The seated incline dumbbell shrug is an alternative to the regular shrug, although some trainees may find the compression of the chest uncomfortable.

Position an adjustable bench at the lowest setting that, when you're face down, allows you to keep your elbows straight and take dumbbells off the floor without forcing a stretch.

While in position on the bench, shrug your shoulders *and* pull them back. Crush your shoulder blades together, then lower the dumbbells under control to the floor, pause for a second, and then start the next rep.

Don't jam your chin onto the bench.

Calf machine shrug—DANGER

For this form of the standing shrug, the resistance rests against the actual musculature that's primarily worked by the exercise. When the musculature contracts, it's distorted because of the compression from the weight. This produces a skewed effect on the musculature, and leads to possible tissue damage. The musculature being worked should be free of compressive impediment to its contraction and relaxation.

The negative effect of the calf machine shrug on the trapezius depends on the design of the calf machine, and the body structure of the individual trainee. There'll probably be a severe pull at the base of the skull regardless of the size of the user or design of the machine. Avoid the calf machine shrug. Use another type of shrug.

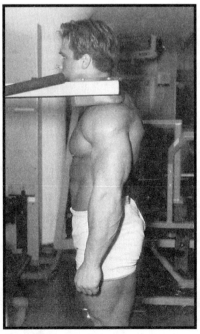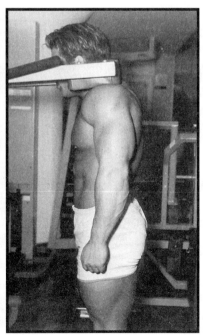

Calf machine shrug—don't use this exercise.

23. SIDE BEND

Main muscles worked

abdominal wall including the quadratus lumborum, erector spinae

Capsule description

hold resistance against a thigh, bend to that side, and return upright

The side bend also provides direct work for some of the small, intervertebral muscles. The side bend works most of the body's core musculature.

The side bend is an asymmetrical exercise. Provided you have a healthy spine free of restrictions, the side bend, when correctly performed, will strengthen your body's core muscles, and increase their robustness, and resistance to injury. If, however, your spinal musculature has restrictions, the side bend will probably be a harmful exercise, and should be avoided.

Perform the side bend with a dumbbell, or a cable from a low pulley.

Dumbbell standing side bend. The range of motion shown here could have been increased had the model moved his hips to his left during the descent to his right side.

A stance a little wider than what's shown here may give greater stability.

Dumbbell side bend

Space your feet about hip-width apart, but fine-tune this to best suit you. If you have a tendency toward groin strains, a close stance with your feet touching may be better. Balance may be harder to maintain with a close stance than a wider one. Keep your buttocks contracted.

A simpler way of doing the dumbbell side bend is while seated at the end of a bench, across the middle of a bench with one foot on each side, or on a box. With a wide enough foot placement to maintain balance, the seated side bend can work well. There'll be no problem with the plates striking your thighs and obstructing performance.

Performance

Take the weight in your right hand. Rest your left hand on your left hip, or external oblique. Bend to your right side as far as feels comfortable, pause for a second, then return to the vertical position. Pause for a second, then repeat. In the standing side bend, as you bend to your right, push your hips to your left. This may help improve stability, and increase the range of motion, too. As you

Dumbbell seated side bend. A wider spacing of the feet than what's illustrated here would give increased stability.

return to the vertical position, move your torso first, then your hips. Do all your reps to your right side without interruption. To exercise the other side of your body, reverse the procedure.

Face forward throughout each set. There should only be lateral movement. Don't lean forward, don't lean back, and don't overstretch.

For stability, distribute the stress over your feet in a 50-50 split. To that end, while you perform the standing side bend, as you descend you should take more of the stress on the inner sides of your feet than the outer.

Do the reps carefully—about three seconds up, and three seconds down, plus a pause for a second at the top, and another at the bottom. Use smooth, controlled movements. Inhale on the descent, and exhale on the ascent, or just breathe freely.

After an intensive set of side bends, take two to three minutes rest before working your other side, so that your performance on the latter doesn't suffer. From workout to workout, alternate the side you work first.

Pulley side bend, standing. The lowest position, left, could be increased if the trainee's hips were pushed out to her left during the descent to her right. The middle photograph shows the usual completion point of a rep—the hips should be symmetrical at this point. Each rep of the side bend can be continued by bending over toward the other side, for further range of motion (right photo).

Pulley side bend

Use a cable that arises from a low pulley. Stand sideways to the apparatus, with the handle in your hand that's nearest to the apparatus. Stand a sufficient distance away from the apparatus so that the plates can't come to rest at the bottom position. And line up the pulley with your ankle, and the direction of the cable with the center of the side of your hips, to keep the resistance in the same vertical plane as your body.

Then follow the guidelines for the dumbbell standing side bend.

General tips for the side bend

Carefully adapt to side bend if you've not done it before, or if you've not done it for a long time. For two weeks, do it two times a week without added resistance. Do a couple of sets of high reps each time. Keep your hands by your sides, then progress to placing them on top of your head. Focus on smooth, controlled reps. Go down to a depth that feels comfortable. If your flexibility increases, you may be able to increase the depth a little during the first few weeks.

To learn the movement, do the exercise sideways to a mirror. Keep your head turned to the side, scrutinize your technique, and ensure lateral movement only. Don't, however, do any intensive side bends with your head turned. You must have your head facing forward when you side bend intensively.

In your third week of side bends, use a light weight and thereafter add poundage slowly and gradually, using small increments.

When you take the resistance to get set up for the side bend—whether a dumbbell, or from a low pulley—keep the stress as symmetrical as possible. Bend your knees, keep your shoulders pulled back, lower back slightly hollowed, and brace your disengaged hand against the thigh on the same side, while the engaged hand takes the resistance from the other side. And reverse the procedure at the end of a set, when you return the resistance to the floor.

Ideally, for the dumbbell side bend, take the 'bell from a dumbbell rack, and set it on a bench rather than the floor. Consequently you would need to bend your knees only slightly in order to take the dumbbell with one hand. Then adopt your stance ready to start the set. At the end of the set, put the dumbbell back on the bench while you rest prior to the next set.

Technique recordings

Periodically, use a video camera and record your exercise technique, for analysis later. A video camera can be an outstanding tool to help improve your exercise technique.

To demonstrate exercise technique clearly, the models sometimes didn't wear shirts, and weight stands and safety bars were often not used. This was for illustration purposes only. When you train, wear a shirt, and take proper safety measures.

24. SQUAT

Two forms of the *barbell* squat will be described. The front squat has the bar held at the front of the shoulders, whereas the back squat has the bar held at the back of the shoulders. The front squat always has the *front* qualifier, whereas the back squat is usually called *the squat* without the *back* qualifier.

Properly done, by trainees without physical limitations or restrictions, the barbell squat is safe and highly effective. But use poor technique, abuse low reps, overtrain, or try to lift a too-heavy weight, and you'll hurt yourself. Learn to squat correctly before you concern yourself with weight, then add weight slowly while maintaining correct technique.

Before you can barbell squat with correct technique, you need to be flexible enough to *adopt* the necessary positioning, and have sufficient back strength to be able to *maintain* the correct back positioning. You especially need flexible calves, hamstrings, thigh adductors, and buttocks. Women who usually wear shoes with high heels are likely to have tight calves. You also need flexible shoulders and pectorals in order to hold the bar in the right position with ease.

If you've had a major back injury, get the clearance of a chiropractor before you barbell squat. If you've had any minor back injuries, still get a chiropractor's clearance.

Two non-barbell forms of the squat will be described: the ball squat, and the hip-belt squat. Neither use a barbell, or resistance on the shoulders.

How to use a power rack

A power rack, correctly used, is perfect for self-spotting, and safety, and can be found in some gyms. A power rack is especially useful for barbell squats, barbell bench press and its variations, deadlifts, and barbell presses. For example, position the pins—or safety bars—an inch or two centimeters below your bottom point of the squat. Then if you can't perform a rep, lower the bar under control to the pins, get out from under the bar, remove the plates, and return the bar to its holders.

The uprights of power racks typically have about two inches or five centimeters between successive holes. If one setting is too high, and the next too low, raise the floor. For the squat, place non-slip rubber matting of the right thickness throughout the floor space within the rack (so that there's no chance of tripping on the edge of the matting).

"Flat back" confusion

The spine is naturally curved when seen from the side. This curvature is the natural, strong structure for absorbing and distributing stress efficiently. When the curves are lost, the strong, load-bearing capability is diminished.

"Keep a flat back" is a common admonition when lifting a weight, and one that I've used in my earlier writing. It's not, however, an accurate one. What it really means, is, "Don't round your lower back." Although it may look like the lower back is flat at the bottom of a correctly performed squat or deadlift, as examples, this is an illusion. When contracted, the spinal erectors, if sufficiently developed, may fill the required slight hollow in the lower back's profile at those bottom positions, giving an impression that the lower back is flat, but the actual *lower spine* should be slightly concave, or hollow.

It's the strong contraction of the lumbar musculature that produces the desired, concave lower back, to create a bracing effect. The strong contraction of the muscles on both sides of the spine not only prevents the forward rounding of the back, but also helps prevent sideways, asymmetrical bending.

If the lower spine is truly flat, the upper back will be rounded, which is a dangerous position when lifting a challenging weight (or even a light one in many cases). A spine that's intentionally straightened while under heavy load bearing, is a weakened one that's exposed to an increased risk of injury. A spine that's naturally straight, suggests pathology.

When lifting a weight, inside or outside of the gym, keep your shoulders retracted, hips pushed back (extended), and lower back slightly hollowed. There are exceptions, however. For example, in the back extension, the back *should* round during the course of this flexion-extension exercise; and during crunches, the lower back shouldn't be hollow—keep it flat against the floor.

Squats, knees, and lower back

Forward travel of the knees is inevitable in squatting, but should be minimized, to reduce stress on the knees. A common guideline for squatting is, during the descent, to avoid the knees traveling forward beyond an imaginary vertical line drawn from the toes. I, too, have recommended this guideline, but few people can follow it for barbell squatting unless they perform partial squats only. The fullest, safe range of motion—safe for the lower back, and the knees—is recommended, and this usually means that the knees will travel forward of the toe line during the barbell squat. Some competitive powerlifters squat with almost vertical shins. They can do this because they have favorable leverages for the squat, use a wide stance, and exaggerate the involvement of their lower backs, and hips. Their goal is to increase their one-rep maximum performances.

The general rule recommended in this book for barbell squatting is to descend until about two inches or five centimeters above the point at which your lower back would start to round. Your back must never round while squatting. For most trainees, provided that controlled rep speed and correct technique are used, this range of motion is safe for the lower back and the knees. For some trainees, this range of motion will mean that the upper thighs will descend to below parallel with the floor, while for most trainees the thighs will descend to parallel with the floor, or a little above parallel.

While learning to use this safe range of motion, it may mean, initially, using a reduced depth of descent. With practice, improved flexibility, and increased strength of your back, you may be able to increase your safe range of motion. Start with just the bare bar when learning how to squat correctly, and progress in resistance gradually.

Footwear reminder

Especially for squats, deadlifts, and overhead presses, you should not wear shoes with thick or spongy soles and heels.

Get yourself a sturdy pair of shoes with good grip to the floor, arch support, and which minimizes deformation when you're lifting heavy weights. No heel elevation relative to the balls of your feet is especially important for squats and deadlifts.

Correct technique to minimize forward travel of the knees while squatting, includes:

1. Wearing a pair of shoes with no heel, or only minimal heel.

2. Not elevating your heels on plates, or a board.

3. Using a medium-width or wider stance—not a close stance.

4. Turning the toes of each foot out at least 20 degrees from the feet-parallel-to-each-other position.

5. Keeping the stress of the weight mostly over your heels—not the balls of your feet.

While applying these guidelines, maintain a slight hollow in your lower back, and minimize forward lean of your torso. Some forward lean of your torso is, however, necessary while barbell squatting.

To minimize forward travel of the knees while squatting, and to keep the back vertical or near vertical, the ball squat, or the hip-belt squat, can be employed. They may be safer forms of the squat for trainees who have knee or back problems when barbell squatting. Properly performed, the ball squat and the hip-belt squat involve little or no loading of the spine.

Knee or lower-back problems may, however, be correctable, with the right therapy.

Squat (back squat)

Main muscles worked

quadriceps, thigh adductors, buttocks, hamstrings, spinal erectors, multifidii

Capsule description

hold a bar over your shoulders, squat, then stand erect

Set-up

Always squat inside a four-post power rack with pins and saddles correctly and securely in place. Alternatively, use a half rack, sturdy and stable squat stands together with spotter racks or bars, or squat rack unit that combines stands and safety bars. Should you fail on a squat, you must be able to descend to the bottom position and safely set the bar down on supports. Make no compromises—*safety comes first*. Ideally, you should have spotters standing by in addition to the aforementioned safety set-up.

There have been terrible injuries among trainees who squatted without a safety set-up, or spotters standing by. When they failed on a rep, they got crushed by the weight before they dumped it, or they toppled forward and severely injured their backs.

A straight bar is fine for squatting, but most trainees may find that a cambered squat bar is better. A cambered bar is bent like that of a yoke. Relative to a straight bar, the bent bar is easier to hold in position, sits better on the upper back, and is less likely to roll out of position. Encourage the management of where you train to get a cambered squat bar. (A skilled metal worker can put a camber in a straight bar.) Straight or cambered, the bar you use for the squat should have knurling around its center, to help you keep it in position during a set.

Cambered squat bar (top), and a straight barbell.

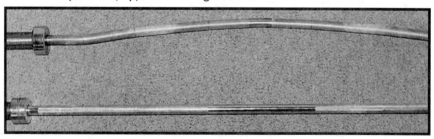

The above right photograph shows the error of shifting stress from over the rear two thirds of the feet (but mostly over the heels), to mostly over the balls of the feet. This has resulted in heel lifting, reduced stability, and exaggerated load on the knees. The model is wearing shoes with thick heels, which has contributed to the technique error.

Safety bars/pins

The safety pins (horizontal bars) have been positioned just above where the barbell is lowered to at the safe, bottom position of the squat for this trainee. Thus, should he fail on a rep—usually during a tough work set—he would lower the barbell to the safety pins, and escape.

From the bottom left, the sequence for the first rep of a set of squats. The final two photographs (bottom right) show the return of the bar to the rack's saddles at the end of the set.

If you can't squat well with a straight bar, a bent bar will probably not make enough difference to warrant the investment. But if you can squat well with a straight bar, you may be able to squat even better with a cambered bar.

Set the bar on its saddles at mid- to upper-chest height. If the bar is too low, you'll waste energy getting it out. If it's too high, you'll need to rise on your toes to get the bar out. The too-high setting is especially dangerous when you return the bar after finishing a hard set of squats.

If you're used to squatting with a straight bar, and move to a cambered bar, you must lower the position of the saddles, and that of the pins or safety bars set at the bottom position of the squat. The ends of a cambered bar are about three inches or eight centimeters lower than the central part that rests on your upper back.

Use little or preferably no padding on the bar. If you're a training novice you'll probably have little visible muscle over and above your shoulder blades. After a few months of progressive training that includes deadlifts and shrugs, you'll start developing the muscular padding required on your upper back. Then the bar can be held in position more comfortably.

The more padding that's around a bar, the more likely that the bar will be incorrectly positioned, or that it will move during a set. Wear a thick sweatshirt rather than a thin T-shirt, to provide acceptable padding to cushion the bar. If more padding is needed, wear a T-shirt and a sweatshirt.

Bar positioning

Before you center the bar on your upper back you must hold the bar properly, with your shoulder blades crushed together. This creates a layer of tensed muscle on your upper back over and above your shoulder blades. Position the bar on the muscle just above the center of the top ridge of your shoulder blades. This is lower than what's typically used by most trainees.

This bar position is essential—to avoid metal to spine contact, and to provide a greater area of contact than that from a higher position. This yields greater bar control.

Practice correct bar positioning until you can do it automatically. What will initially feel awkward, will become relatively comfortable after a few weeks of practice.

Good bar placement for the squat (left). Bar too high and hands not holding it properly (right). A cambered bar may not drape over your shoulders properly (left) unless there's weight pulling on it.

Grip

Hold the bar securely in your hands, not loosely in the tips of your fingers. Don't drape your wrists over the bar, or hands over the plates. Furthermore, each hand must be the same distance from the center of the bar.

The width of grip depends on your torso size, forearm and arm lengths, and shoulder and pectoral flexibility. For the best control over the bar, use the closest grip that feels comfortable. But if your grip is too close, it will be hard on your shoulders and elbows.

If your grip is too wide, you'll risk trapping your fingers between the bar and the safety supports or rack pins at the bottom of the squat. Place your hands so that there's no chance of your fingers getting trapped.

Stance

Following experimentation using a *bare* bar, find *your* optimum width of heel placement, and degree of toe flare. As a starting point, place your feet hip-width apart and parallel with each other, then turn out the toes on *each* foot about 30 degrees. Perform some squats. Then try a bit more flare and the same heel spacing. Next, try a slightly wider stance, and the initial toe flare. Then try the wider stance with more flare.

The combination of a moderate stance and well-flared toes usually gives plenty of room to squat into, helps to prevent excessive forward lean, and lets you squat deeper without your lower back

Left, feet too close. Middle, feet well spaced but with insufficient flare. Right, this stance for the squat, or something close to it, will work well for most trainees. The bar is positioned too high in these photos, and the back isn't properly set.

rounding. But too-wide a stance will restrict your descent. Experiment until you find the stance that best suits you. Individual variation in leg and thigh lengths, torso length, hip girth, and relative lengths of legs and thighs, contribute to determining the squat stance that's ideal for you. Tall trainees usually need a wider stance than trainees of average height.

Find a foot placement that spreads the stress of the squat over your thighs, buttocks, and back. Squat without your lower back rounding, your torso leaning forward excessively, or your heels coming off the floor. There should be no tendency to topple forward. Keep forward movement of your knees to a minimum, and keep your knees pointing in the *same* direction as your feet. Don't let your knees buckle inward.

If you have a stance that's too close, or has insufficient toe flare, then buckling of your knees may be inevitable when you squat intensively.

It may take a few workouts before you find the best stance for you. With just a bare bar over your upper back, stand on some cardboard, adopt your squat stance, and check it out. After tinkering with your stance, once you're sure it's correct, and while keeping your feet in position, get someone to draw the outline of your feet on the card. Then you'll have a record of your stance for when you want to refer to it. Practice repeatedly until you can adopt your squat stance automatically.

The right-side pair of photographs shows the correct stance—heels well spaced, and toes flared. The far-right photographs show an incorrect stance—feet close together, and parallel with each other. Notice how the incorrect, cramped stance increases forward travel of the knees, and forward lean of the torso.

The bar is positioned too high in these four photographs.

Initial performance

Face the bar so that you have to walk *backward* from the saddles before taking your squatting stance. Take your grip on the bar, and get under it as it rests on the weight saddles or stands. Don't lean over to get under the bar. Bend your knees, and get your torso and hips underneath the bar. Your feet can either be hip-width apart under the bar, or split. If split, one foot will be a little in front of the bar, and the other will be a little behind the bar. Pull your scapulae together, tense the musculature of your back, and position the bar correctly.

Your lower back should be slightly hollowed, and your hips directly under the bar. Look forward, tense your entire torso, then straighten your knees. The bar should move *vertically* out of the saddles or stands.

Stand still for a few seconds. Check that the bar feels correctly centered. If it feels heavier on one side than the other, put it back on the saddles. If it felt a little unbalanced, stay under the bar as it rests on the saddles, reposition the bar, and try again. If, however, it felt considerably lopsided, get out from under the bar, check that you loaded the bar correctly, and make any necessary corrections. Then get under the bar again, position it properly, and unrack it.

Never walk out of squat stands with a bar that doesn't feel properly centered on your upper back.

Step back the minimum distance so that you don't hit the uprights of the rack or squat stands during the ascent. Don't step forward after you've taken the bar out of its supports. If you do, you'll have to walk backward and look to the rear to return the bar to its supports. This is more hazardous than returning the bar forward to its supports.

Slide your feet over the floor as you walk with the bar. This keeps both of your feet in constant contact with the floor. Put your feet in the stance you've drilled yourself to adopt. Don't look down. At all times while standing with the bar, whether stationary or moving into your stance, maintain a natural degree of lower-back inward curve. Never slouch. Maintenance of the natural strong curves of your spine is critical for back health, when bearing weight.

Keep your jaw parallel with the floor—during and between reps. Your eyes should look straight ahead or slightly up, but not down. Fix your eyes on one spot throughout a set.

The weight should be felt mostly through your heels, not the front of your feet, but don't rock back on your heels and lose your balance.

Descent

With the bar, center of your hips, and heels in a vertical line, weight felt mostly through your heels, unlock your knees and sit down and back. The knee and hip breaks should be simultaneous. Maintain a tight, tensed back, with your shoulder blades retracted, and make a deliberate effort to tense your back further as you descend. Push your chest out as you descend, and push your hips to the rear. Doing all of this will help to maintain the slightly hollowed lower back, which is essential for safe, effective squatting.

Descend symmetrically, under control, with the weight felt mostly through your heels. Take about three seconds to descend to your bottom position.

Left, squat to a depth where the upper thighs are parallel with the floor. The lower spine is still slightly hollowed, albeit the hollow is filled with muscle. This is the maximum safe depth for this trainee. Middle, the increased depth has caused the lower back to round. Right, severe rounding or flexion of the lower spine. DANGER: never allow your back to round in the squat. The right photograph also illustrates the incorrect shift of the stress from the exercise to mostly over the balls of the feet, and exaggerated forward travel of the knees, whereas the left-most photograph illustrates stress mostly over the heels.

Some forward movement of your knees and shins is necessary, but keep it to the minimum. Keeping the weight felt mostly through your heels helps to maintain correct leg positioning. Provided that correct technique is used, how much forward movement there is of your knees largely depends on your body structure and how deep you squat.

Depth of descent

With poor squatting technique, your lower back will round earlier in the descent than it would had you used correct technique. With correct set-up and technique, as described here, and just a bare bar, find the depth of descent at which your lower back just starts to round. An assistant must watch you from the side, with his eyes level with your hips at your bottom position.

Set your squatting depth at two inches or five centimeters above the point where your lower back just starts to round. Position the safety bars of the power rack, or squat stands, at that depth.

When the hips rise faster than the shoulders, the torso tips forward excessively, and stress is greatly exaggerated on the lower back—DANGER. Your hips must not rise faster than your shoulders.

Ideally, descend until your upper thighs are parallel with or just below parallel with the floor. If your lower back starts to round before you reach the parallel position, you mustn't squat to parallel. Most trainees who are flexible enough, and who use correct technique, can squat to parallel without their lower backs rounding. Don't reduce your squatting depth except for safety reasons. The deeper you squat, the less weight you'll need to exhaust the involved musculature.

Although some trainees can squat safely to well below parallel, they belong to a minority. You may belong to that minority. Squatting to below parallel is called the *full squat.*

Ascent

Don't pause at the bottom position. Immediately start the ascent. Ascend while pushing mostly through your heels. Push with equal force through both feet. If you favor one side, you may produce asymmetrical motion in your ascent, which is dangerous. Take two to three seconds for each ascent.

During the ascent, the bar as seen from the side should move vertically. It mustn't move forward before it moves upward. If you tip forward at the bottom of the squat, the bar will go forward before it starts to go up. This is a common mistake, and has produced many lower-back injuries.

Your hips must not rise faster than your shoulders.

Knees coming in on the ascent is a common symptom of set-up flaws in the squat. Insufficient toe flare, and heels too close, are common flaws responsible for buckling of the knees. Tight thigh adductors may also contribute.

Heel elevation—DANGER

Squatting with the heels elevated is a mistake. Some trainees elevate their heels under the belief that they will isolate certain areas of their quadriceps. Others do it to maintain their balance, to compensate for insufficient flexibility, or poor squatting technique.

Safe squatting involves distributing the weight over the rear two thirds of each foot, and pushing primarily through the heels on the ascent. When the heels are elevated, the balls of the feet take more of the weight, forward travel of the knees is increased unnecessarily, and the hips and knees shift forward, which corrupts the balanced spread of stress over the thighs, buttocks, and back. The result is unnecessarily increased knee stress, with potentially harmful consequences.

The flexibility work recommended in this book will help address the insufficient flexibility that's often at the root of trainees' desire for heel elevation while squatting. When adequate flexibility is combined with good squatting technique—including the right width of stance, and degree of toe flare—the heels will stay where they belong: on the floor.

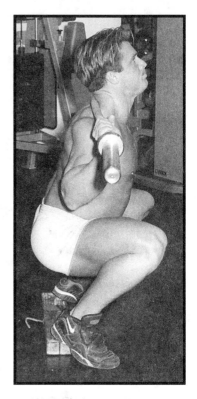

Never squat with a board, plate, or block under your heels. Raising your heels produces a more upright torso, but distorts the balanced spread of stress over the thighs, hips, and back. The result is unnecessarily increased knee stress, with potentially harmful consequences.

Focus on pushing mostly through your heels. This will help you maintain the proper ascent. Pushing through the front part of your feet will almost inevitably tip you forward, and ruin your ascent. Make a special effort to keep your shoulder blades pulled back, your chest pushed out, and hips pushed to the rear, to help you keep your ascent in the right groove.

The ascent, like the descent, should be symmetrical. The bar shouldn't tip to one side, and you shouldn't take more weight on one side of your body than the other.

While standing

Pause briefly to take one or more deep breaths, then move into the next rep. While standing between reps, don't sway at your hips, don't rock the bar on your shoulders, don't take more of the weight on one foot than the other, and don't rotate your hips. Stay rigid, with the weight distributed symmetrically, and maintain the natural inward curve in your lower spine. If you move your hips forward during the pause between reps, you'll flatten the curve at the bottom of your spine and greatly weaken your back.

While standing between reps, preserve the natural curves of your spine (left). Don't round your back (right).

Racking the bar

At the end of a set, rack the bar. While sliding your feet so that you always have both feet in contact with the floor, shuffle forward until the bar is directly above the saddles or stands. Check that you're not going to miss the bar holders with the bar, and ensure that your fingers aren't lined up to be trapped between the bar and its holders. Then bend your knees and set the bar down.

The bar should be returned to its holders in a vertical motion. A common error is to stop short of the saddles or stands and lower the bar through leaning forward while keeping the knees straight. This is dangerous. It leads to reduced control over the bar, and excessive stress on a tired back.

Other tips

Don't squat in a sweaty shirt. Change your shirt before you squat, if need be. Don't squat with a bare torso, because it reduces the stability of the bar on your back.

Before you get under the bar for a work set, put chalk or rosin on your hands, and perhaps get someone to put chalk or rosin on your shirt where the bar will rest. This may help the bar to stay in position.

Increasing your shoulder and pectoral flexibility will help you to hold the bar in position with less difficulty.

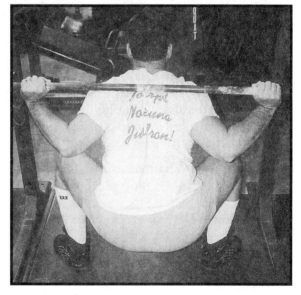

Good squatting form—down to parallel while maintaining good back positioning, and minimal forward travel of the knees.

Practice, practice, and practice again, with just a bare bar, until you can get into your correct squatting stance without having to look down or fiddle around to get your feet in the right position.

Never turn your head while you're squatting. If you do, the bar will tip slightly, your groove will be spoiled, and you could hurt yourself.

The orthodox breathing pattern when squatting is to take one or more deep breaths while standing, descend, and then exhale during the ascent. If you're squatting for 10 or fewer reps, then one or two deep breaths before each rep should suffice. For longer-duration sets, take three deep breaths before reps 11 through 15, and three or four deep breaths before reps 16 through 20.

Don't squat to a bench, box, or chair, as that would cause compression of your spine because your vertebrae would get squeezed between the weight up top and the hard surface down below. You could, however, squat to a soft object of the right height for you, such as a large piece of soft packing foam. When you feel the foam brushing against your buttocks or hamstrings, depending on where the foam is placed, you'll have reached your maximum safe depth but without risk of spinal compression.

To help you to improve your squatting technique, record yourself with a video camera, from the side view. Watching yourself in a mirror isn't adequate alone.

Once you've mastered the technique, give 100% attention to ensure that you deliver correct technique on every rep. Just a slight slip of concentration can lead to lowering the bar out of position, one hand getting ahead or in front of the other, or one thigh taking more load than the other.

Don't squat if your lower back is sore from an earlier workout, or heavy manual labor. Wait until you've recovered. Furthermore, don't perform any form of deadlift before you squat. Don't fatigue your lower back and reduce its potential as a major stabilizer for the squat.

Don't use a lifting belt. It's not required.

Spotting

As soon as the bar stalls, moves laterally, tips, or the squatter starts to twist to one side, the spotter or spotters must act to prevent the rep deteriorating further. If there are no spotters, set the bar down immediately (under control) on the safety bars. Don't try to complete a squat unassisted when your technique has started to break down.

If two spotters are involved, there must be excellent communication and synchronized action. If one spotter shouts "Take it!" the other must respond even if the latter thinks the assistance could have been delayed. Assistance needs to be applied equally to each side, to maintain a horizontal bar.

If one spotter is involved, he should stand directly behind the trainee. Assistance is given by the spotter standing astride the trainee, grabbing him or her around the lower rib cage, maintaining bent

Spotting for the squat.

knees and a slightly arched back, and applying upward pressure. This will work only if a little help is needed to get the trainee through the sticking point. It's no way of providing a lot of assistance when the trainee is exhausted. It is, however, a quick way of injuring the spotter because he'll end up leaning forward and heavily stressing his lower back. A single spotter shouldn't even try to help you up if substantial assistance is needed. Instead, the spotter should help you to lower the bar safely to the rack pins or safety bars.

Even if the spotter doesn't need to assist during a rep, he should be alert to help guide the bar back into the weight saddles after the final rep. At the end of a hard set of squats, you'll be tired. Without a pair of guiding hands on the bar from a spotter you may miss getting the bar into the weight saddles.

Patience

It may take time for the squat to feel natural. Don't lose heart if you find that squatting with the bare bar feels awkward, and you wobble a lot. But don't go adding a lot of weight prematurely. Build up gradually, and be confident that the exercise will feel better later than it does at first.

How to improve your ability to squat

Only a small proportion of trainees are naturally gifted for back squatting and front squatting, largely because of their body proportions and leverages. Most trainees need to work at squatting technique *and* the essential supportive work, to make themselves into competent squatters.

There are three major components of good squatting ability:

1. The flexibility to be able to *adopt* the correct body positioning.

2. The back strength to be able to *maintain* the correct back positioning.

3. Correct exercise technique.

You need sufficient flexibility in the major musculature of your lower body, along with the required shoulder flexibility to hold the bar in position correctly. Follow the flexibility program in this book. If any of the muscles have anything less than at least a normal, healthy level of flexibility, squatting technique will probably be compromised, with a reduction in safety and productivity. Squat correctly, or not at all.

You need sufficient strength throughout your back—lower, middle, and upper—to be able to hold your lower back in the required slightly hollowed position during the squat. This is critical for safety. Your back must not round while squatting—there must be no back flexion. Four key back exercises—deadlift, back extension, row, and shrug—will help build the required back strength provided that they are worked with correct technique, and progressive resistance.

Having the required flexibility and back strength is one thing, but learning to *use* the flexibility and strength during the squat is something else.

It may take several months before correct squatting technique can be implemented, even with minimal weight. Don't be frustrated to begin with. As your flexibility and back strength improve, and your ability to use them, so will your squatting ability. Until you can adopt the correct squatting technique, keep the resistance very light—perhaps just the bare bar. Thereafter, as your squatting weight grows, so should your strength in the deadlift, back extension, row, and shrug, to help you to maintain the correct back positioning.

The Smith machine

Smith machine squats give only an illusion of safety relative to the barbell squat. With the Smith machine, the bar is locked into a fixed pathway so you don't have to be concerned with balance; and you don't have to take a barbell from stands, step back to perform your set, and step forward at the end of a set in order to return the bar to the stands. But when you look further into the Smith machine squat, there are perils.

Don't squat in the Smith machine. Its use is loaded with dangerous compromises. It forces you to follow the bar path dictated by the machine, but the bar path should be dictated by your body.

If you put your feet forward in the Smith machine squat, to prevent your knees travelling too far forward at the bottom of the movement relative to your feet, you would put your lower back at risk. If your feet are well forward, you would lose the natural, required slight hollow in your lower back—including at the bottom of the movement—because your hips would be forward of their ideal position. Although your knees may be spared some stress, it would be at the cost of a back injury, sooner or later.

If you bring your feet back so that they are directly beneath your shoulders, all may look well until you descend. Then your knees would travel forward excessively, the load would shift more to over the balls of your feet, the stress on your knees would be exaggerated, and the risk of injury would increase.

When used for full-range movements such as the squat, bench press, incline bench press, and overhead press, correct exercise technique is corrupted by the vertical bar pathway that the Smith machine enforces. This will set you up for injuries.

Used correctly, free-weights provide the freedom required to move through pathways that are natural for your body.

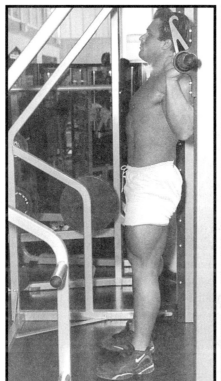

Don't squat in the Smith machine because the rigid, vertical pathway corrupts natural squatting technique. This is hostile to the back and the knees.

Front squat

Main muscles worked

quadriceps, thigh adductors, buttocks, hamstrings, spinal erectors, multifidii

Capsule description

hold a bar at the front of your shoulders, squat, then stand erect

Set-up

Always front squat inside a four-post power rack with pins and saddles correctly and securely in place. Alternatively, use a half rack, sturdy and stable squat stands together with spotter racks or bars, or a squat rack unit that combines stands and safety bars. Should you fail on a front squat, you must be able to descend to the bottom position and safely set the bar down on supports. Make no compromises—*safety comes first.* Ideally, you should have spotters standing by in addition to the aforementioned safety set-up.

Position the bar saddles so that the barbell (straight, not cambered) is set at mid- to upper-chest height. If the bar is too low, you'll waste energy getting it out. If it's too high, you'll need to rise on your toes to get the bar out. The too-high setting is especially dangerous when you return the bar after finishing a hard set of front squats.

Wear a thick sweatshirt rather than a thin T-shirt, to provide padding to cushion the bar where it rests on your deltoids next to your clavicles. Some of the weight will end up on your clavicles, but not all—minimize it, to prevent excessive discomfort. If more padding is needed, wear a T-shirt and a sweatshirt.

Bar positioning

To find where the bar should sit during the front squat, lift your left arm out in front so that your left elbow is higher than your left shoulder. Then with your right hand find the groove where your left front deltoid meets your left collar bone. That's the groove where the bar should sit—mostly on the deltoid, not the clavicle. Place a bare bar there, to get the feel for it.

To keep the bar in position, cross your hands on the bar—left hand over the bar on your right side, and right hand over the bar on your

left side. The bar should be just in front of your windpipe. Keep your hands firmly on the bar, and elbows higher than your shoulders. This elbow positioning is critical, to maintain a sufficiently upright torso to prevent the bar falling forward and out of position. If your elbows drop, your technique will crumble.

Because of the use of a closer hand spacing in the front squat than the back squat, a shorter bar than an Olympic one may be easier to handle. If you have a shorter bar available, and the stands to support it between sets (or assistants to help you), try that for the front squat.

Stance

Following experimentation using a bare bar, find your optimum width of heel placement, and degree of toe flare. As a starting point, place your feet hip-width apart and parallel with each other, then turn out the toes on each foot about 30 degrees. Perform some front squats. Then try a bit more flare and the same heel spacing. Next, try a slightly wider stance, and the initial toe flare. Then try the wider stance with more flare.

Too close a stance will hamper stability, and too wide a stance will restrict your descent. Experiment until you find the stance that best suits you. Individual variation in leg and thigh lengths, torso length, hip girth, and relative lengths of your legs and thighs, contribute to determining the front squat stance that's ideal for you. The stance you settle on may be a little closer than what you would use in the back squat.

Find a foot placement that provides stability, the fullest *safe* range of motion, no rounding of your lower back, and minimal forward lean. Your heels must remain fixed to the floor. You need to be stable, with no tendency to topple forward. Never put a board or plates under your heels.

Keep your knees pointing in the same direction as your feet. Don't let your knees buckle inward.

If your stance is too close, or has insufficient flare, then buckling of your knees may be inevitable when you front squat intensively.

Fine-tune your stance, and keep working on your buttock, hamstring, and calf flexibility. As you loosen up over a few weeks, along with fine-tuning your stance, your front squatting technique will improve. Don't lose heart if it's difficult to begin with.

It may take a few workouts before you find the best stance for you. When you've got it, stand on some cardboard, and adopt your front squat stance. Get someone to draw the outline of your feet on the card. Then you'll have a record of your stance for when you want to refer to it. Practice repeatedly until you can adopt your front squat stance automatically, without having to look down to check where your feet are.

Initial performance

Face the bar so that you have to walk backward from the saddles before taking your squatting stance. Get under the bar as it rests on the weight saddles or stands. Don't lean over to get under the bar. Bend your knees and get your hips underneath the bar. Place your feet directly beneath the bar, side-by-side a bit wider than shoulder-width apart. Pull your scapulae together, tense the musculature of your back, keep your lower back slightly hollowed, then position the bar. Remember, the bar should sit mostly on your deltoids, not your clavicles.

Cross your hands on the bar—left hand over the bar on your right side, and right hand over the bar on your left side. Hold your head and neck upright, to prevent the bar jamming into your windpipe. This will take time to adapt to, and require a number of workouts. At all times, keep your hands firmly on the bar, and elbows higher than your shoulders. Fight to do it. Then your control will be good.

With the bar in position, your lower back slightly hollowed, scapulae pulled together, and your hips directly under the bar, look forward, tense your torso, then straighten your knees. The bar should move vertically out of the saddles or stands. Don't unrack the bar in an inclined pathway. Stand still for a few seconds, without moving your feet. Check that the bar feels correctly centered. If it feels heavier on one side than the other, put it back on the saddles, reposition it, and try again. If it felt considerably lopsided, get out from under the bar, check that you have loaded the bar correctly, and make any necessary corrections. Then get under the bar again, position it correctly, and unrack it.

Step back the minimum distance so that you don't hit the uprights of the rack or squat stands during the ascent. Don't step forward after you've taken the bar out of its supports. If you do, you'll have to walk backward to return the bar to its supports. This is more hazardous than returning the bar forward into the rack saddles or squat stands.

Slide your feet over the floor as you walk with the bar. This keeps both your feet in constant contact with the floor. Then put your feet in the stance you've drilled yourself to adopt. Don't look down.

At all times, keep your hands firmly on the bar, and elbows higher than your shoulders. Fight to do it. Then your control of the bar should be good.

Keep your jaw parallel with the floor—during and between reps. Your eyes should look straight ahead or slightly up, but not down. Fix your eyes on a spot throughout the set.

The weight should be felt mostly through your heels, but don't rock back on your heels and lose your balance.

Caution—bar tipping

Because the hands are closer in the front squat than the back squat, and because the bar may rest on a narrower area in the former, the bar tips more readily in the front squat than the back squat. Although the bar should be horizontal for every exercise—for symmetrical distribution of stress—special care is required to maintain it in the front squat.

Descent

With the bar, center of your hips, and heels in a vertical line, weight felt mostly through your heels, unlock your knees and sit down and back. The knee and hip breaks should be simultaneous.

Maintain a tight, tensed back, with your shoulder blades retracted, and make a deliberate effort to tense your back further as you descend. Stick your chest out as you descend, and push your hips to the rear. Doing all of this will help to maintain the slightly hollowed lower back, which is critical for safe, effective front squatting.

At all times, keep your hands firmly on the bar, and elbows higher than your shoulders. Fight to do it. Then your control of the bar should be good.

Descend symmetrically, under control, and with the weight felt mostly through your heels. Take about three seconds to descend to your full, safe, front squatting depth.

Some forward movement of your knees is a necessity, but keep it to the minimum. Provided that correct technique is used, how much forward movement there is of your knees largely depends on your body structure, and how deep you squat.

Depth of descent

With poor front squatting technique, your lower back will round earlier in the descent than it would had you used correct technique. With correct set-up and technique, as described in this section, and just a bare bar, find the depth of descent at which your lower back just starts to round. An assistant must watch you from the side, with his eyes level with your hips at your bottom position.

Set your depth at two inches or five centimeters above the point where rounding of your lower back just starts. Position the safety bars of the power rack, or squat stands, at that depth.

Ideally, descend until your upper thighs are parallel with or just below parallel with the floor. Most trainees who are flexible enough can front squat to parallel or a bit below without their lower backs rounding.

Don't reduce your front squatting depth except for safety reasons. The deeper you front squat, the less weight you'll need to exhaust the involved musculature. Most trainees can front squat deeper than they back squat before their lower backs start to round.

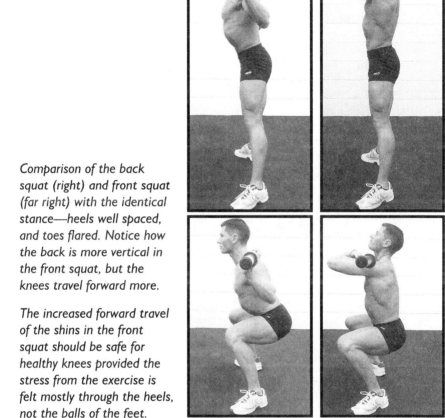

Comparison of the back squat (right) and front squat (far right) with the identical stance—heels well spaced, and toes flared. Notice how the back is more vertical in the front squat, but the knees travel forward more.

The increased forward travel of the shins in the front squat should be safe for healthy knees provided the stress from the exercise is felt mostly through the heels, not the balls of the feet.

Ascent

As soon as you reach your bottom position, push up in a controlled manner, with equal force through the heels of both feet. If you favor one side, you may produce an asymmetrical ascent, which is dangerous. Take two to three seconds for each ascent.

At all times, keep your hands firmly on the bar, and elbows higher than your shoulders. Fight to do it. Then your control of the bar should be good.

During the ascent, the bar, as seen from the side, should move vertically. It mustn't move forward before it moves upward. If you tip forward at the bottom of the front squat, the bar will go forward before it starts to go up. This is a common mistake that causes loss of bar control, which produces lower-back injuries, and other problems.

Your hips must not rise faster than your shoulders. Lead with your head and shoulders.

Focus on pushing mostly through your heels. This will help you to maintain the proper ascent. Pushing through the front part of your feet will almost inevitably tip you forward, and ruin your ascent. Make a special effort to keep your shoulder blades pulled back, chest stuck out, and hips pushed to the rear, to help you keep your ascent in the right groove.

The ascent, like the descent, should be symmetrical. The bar shouldn't tip to one side, and you shouldn't take more weight on one side of your body than the other.

While standing

Pause briefly to take one or more deep breaths, then move into the next rep. While standing between reps, don't sway at your hips, don't rock the bar on your shoulders, don't take more of the weight on one foot than the other, and don't rotate your hips. Stay rigid, with the weight distributed symmetrically, and maintain the natural inward curve in your lower spine. If you move your hips forward during the pause between reps, you'll flatten the curve at the bottom of your spine, and greatly weaken your back.

Once again . . . *keep your hands firmly on the bar, and elbows higher than your shoulders. Fight to do it. Then your control of the bar should be good.*

Racking the bar

At the end of a set, rack the bar. While sliding your feet so that you always have both feet in contact with the floor, shuffle forward until the bar is directly above the saddles or stands. Check that you're not going to miss the bar holders with the bar, and ensure that your fingers aren't lined up to be trapped between the bar and its holders. Then bend your knees and set the bar down.

The bar should be returned to its holders in a vertical motion. A common error is to stop short of the saddles or stands and lower the bar through leaning forward while keeping the knees straight. This is dangerous. It leads to reduced control over the bar, and excessive stress on a tired back.

Other tips

Never turn your head while you're lifting or lowering the bar. If you do, the bar will tip slightly, your groove will be spoiled, and you could hurt yourself.

The orthodox breathing pattern when front squatting is to take one or more deep breaths while standing, descend, and then exhale during the ascent. Alternatively, breathe freely.

Consolidating front squatting technique takes time and patience. With a bare bar, practice on alternate days for as many sessions as it takes until you master the technique. Then build up the resistance slowly and carefully.

Expect awkwardness with the positioning of the bar. You must persist with the front squat. Don't give up after a brief trial. With a bit of practice you *will* adjust—you'll find the precise position for the bar that will work for you. A small adjustment in bar position can make a big difference. What may have felt impossible to begin with may, a few weeks later, feel fine.

If, however, after six weeks of persistence, holding the bar in position still feels too uncomfortable, use a little padding between the bar and your deltoids additional to what you get from your clothing. Tightly wrap a small towel around the bar before putting the bar in place on your shoulders or, better yet, slip a thin strip of compressed foam tubing over the center of the bar. Don't use a large towel or thick piece of foam (whether soft or compressed), as both lead to incorrect bar positioning, and bar movement on your shoulders during a set, which will ruin your technique.

One last time: *Keep your hands firmly on the bar, and elbows higher than your shoulders. Fight to do it. Then your control of the bar should be good.*

As observed from the side view of the front squat, get feedback from a training partner. Alternatively, record yourself with a video camera. Watching your reflection in a mirror isn't adequate for analyzing your front squatting technique.

Once you've mastered the technique, give 100% attention to ensure that you deliver correct technique during every rep. Just a slight slip of concentration can lead to lowering the bar out of position, the elbows dropping beneath shoulder height, or one foot taking more load than the other. Any of these will spoil the pathway of the bar, make the weight feel heavier, make your reps harder, cause frustration, and risk injury.

Don't front squat to a bench, box, or chair, as that would cause compression of your spine because your vertebrae would get squeezed between the weight up top and the hard surface down below.

Don't front squat if your lower back is sore from an earlier workout, or heavy manual labor. Wait until you've recovered. Furthermore, don't perform any form of deadlift before you front squat. Don't fatigue your lower back and reduce its potential as a major stabilizer for the front squat.

Don't use a lifting belt. It's not required.

Safety reminders

Always back and front squat inside a four-post power rack with pins and saddles correctly and securely in place. Alternatively, use a half rack, sturdy and stable squat stands together with spotter racks or bars, or a squat rack unit that combines stands and safety bars. Use a set-up so that should you fail on a squat, you can descend to the bottom position and safely set the bar down on the supports. There must be no compromise here—*safety comes first*. Ideally, you should have spotters standing by in addition to the aforementioned safety set-up.

To demonstrate exercise technique clearly, the models sometimes didn't wear shirts, and weight stands and safety bars were often not used. This was for illustration purposes only. When you train, wear a shirt, and take proper safety measures.

Ball squat

Main muscles worked

quadriceps, thigh adductors, buttocks, hamstrings

Capsule description

stand with a ball between your hips and a wall, squat, then stand erect

The ball squat, also called the *wall squat*, is an alternative to the barbell squat that doesn't heavily involve the lower back. It's technically easier than the back squat and front squat, and requires minimal equipment.

Set-up and positioning

Obtain a soft, exercise or stability ball 12 to 16 inches (or 30 to 40 centimeters) in diameter. Stand on a non-slip surface, parallel with an area of a smooth wall that has no objects mounted on it, facing away from the wall. Position the center of the ball between your hips and the wall. Stand upright, with the ball snugly in place, and your heels about hip-width apart. Next, move your feet forward four to five inches, and turn your toes out about 30 degrees on each side.

You may need to try several exercise balls to find one that works best for you. The ideal size of the ball varies according to the size of the individual. A large person will require a larger ball. The degree of preferred softness may vary, too.

Performance

Keep your torso vertical, head up, eyes forward, shoulders retracted, and lower back slightly hollowed, and take about three seconds to sit down to the point where your upper thighs are approximately parallel with the floor. Pause for a second, then smoothly ascend to the starting position, pushing only through your heels. Pushing only through your heels minimizes the stress on the knee joints. Again, keep your torso vertical, head up, eyes forward, shoulders retracted, and lower back slightly hollowed. And keep your shoulders directly above your hips throughout each rep. Take two to three seconds for each ascent. At the top of each rep, either gently fully straighten your knees, or keep them slightly bent. Pause for a second at the top, then descend into the next rep.

Your knees should point in the same direction as your toes. Don't allow your knees to move inward.

As you descend and ascend, the ball will move up and down your back. Keep the ball centered on your back. And keep your body moving symmetrically. Lean against the ball the minimum amount— just enough to maintain balance and correct positioning.

Fine-tune the set-up position so that during each descent your shins remain vertical, or close to vertical, and your knees and hips feel comfortable. Minimize forward travel of your knees. Depending on your height and body proportions, you may need to move your feet forward a little further, widen your stance a little more, and turn out your toes a little further. You may also benefit from fine-tuning the ball position—probably by lowering its starting position. And remember to push through your heels on the ascent.

Make one change at a time, and perform a few reps following each change. Perform one or two sets, ten reps per set, each rep to approximately parallel with the floor.

If, the following day, you have no negative reaction in your knees or hips, try a greater range of motion the next workout—descend to below the parallel position, but not so low that your lower back rounds. Find the maximum range of motion for you that keeps your lower back slightly hollowed, and is comfortable for your knees and hips. This range of motion will probably be greater in the ball squat than in the back squat or front squat.

If, however, you had a negative reaction in your hips or knees, don't increase your range of motion. Instead, once your joints feel fine, test the exercise again, but adjust your foot positioning to try to find a safer set-up.

Once you've found a safe set-up, and maximum range of motion for you, gradually increase your performance. When you can perform three sets of 15 reps, start to use additional resistance. Hold a dumbbell in each hand as you perform the ball squat, with your palms parallel with each other. Keep your forearms and arms straight and vertical—consider them as links to the dumbbells.

The ball may ride up your back during the set, and need to be lowered. If so, and if you're holding additional resistance, get an assistant to lower the ball quickly while you stand upright.

Lean the minimum amount against the ball—just enough to maintain balance and correct positioning. Excessive leaning into the ball changes the dynamics of the exercise, and may increases stress on your knees.

The orthodox breathing pattern when squatting is to take one or more deep breaths while standing, descend, and then exhale during the ascent. Alternatively, breathe freely.

Other tips

Take the dumbbells from the floor at the bottom of the first ball squat, or from low bases. Thereafter keep hold of the dumbbells until the bottom position of the final rep, when you would return them to their starting positions. When you're at your maximum, safe, bottom position of each rep, the dumbbells should just brush the floor or elevation. Whether you'll need bases will depend on your limb and torso lengths, and their relative proportions, depth of squatting, and size of the dumbbells. If the dumbbells would be too low for you when on the floor, elevate each of them on one or more plates, smooth sides up.

In some cases, the dumbbells may strike the floor before the trainee has reached the bottom position. In this case, the lifter needs to be elevated sufficiently—for instance, on a side-by-side pair of large weight plates turned smooth sides up—so that the dumbbells are in the correct position on the floor for taking at the bottom of the first rep.

Don't lean to one side to pick up a dumbbell. Keep yourself symmetrical. Furthermore, don't descend deeper than your usual depth to get the dumbbells on your first rep.

With weighty dumbbells, use chalk or rosin on your hands. If the dumbbell handles have sharp knurling, that will help your grip greatly, especially if you have chalk or rosin on your hands, too.

An alternative to using a pair of dumbbells is to suspend securely a single dumbbell, or weight plates, from a chain or rope attached to a belt around your hips. The belt could be the same one used for parallel bar dips—a purpose-made weight belt. You'd probably need to stand on two stable platforms so that the suspended dumbbell or weight plates don't hit the floor before you reach your bottom position.

The squat with suspended resistance but without use of a ball for support, is called a *hip-belt squat*, and is described next.

Hip-belt squat

Main muscles worked

quadriceps, thigh adductors, buttocks, hamstrings

Capsule description

stand with resistance suspended from your hips and between your legs, hold a support, squat, then stand erect

The hip-belt squat is another alternative to the barbell squat that doesn't heavily involve the lower back if done correctly. It provides tremendous work for the thighs and buttocks. It usually permits a deeper squat than can be safely tolerated in the barbell squat because with the hip-belt squat there's rearward movement of the torso, little or no forward lean of the torso, minimal involvement of the lower back, and reduced forward travel of the knees.

Set-up and positioning

Find or make two sturdy, broad, *non-slip* platforms, to stand on. If there's any wobble of the platforms, wedge shims under one or more of the corners. The platforms should be at least 15 inches tall, preferably over 20. The lower the resistance hangs from your body, the more comfortable the set-up may feel, but the more easily the weight will swing. Use a rep speed slow enough to prevent the weight swinging.

Until you're using about 125 to 150 pounds (57 to 68 kilos), a belt for attaching weight for the parallel bar dip can substitute for a hip belt. But beyond that weight, or earlier in some cases, a proper hip belt—a heavy-duty weight belt with special attachments—is recommended, for comfort and safety. A supplier of such a hip belt is www.ironmind.com.

With a hip belt the weight stack may be attached by straps or chain to the front *and* rear of the belt, and there may be reduced friction between your body, belt, and attachments compared with other belts. If front *and* rear attachments are used, the length of the one between the rear of the belt and the loading pin will be longer than that of the front one, maybe by three to four inches. Some trainees may prefer to attach the loading pin to the front of the hip belt only, rather than the front *and* the rear.

Some trainees may fix the attachments to the hip belt using carabiners (spring clips), but others may fix them directly to the hip belt, and use a carabiner only to make the connection with the loading pin. Multiple carabiners, perhaps of different sizes, could be linked to fine tune the total length of an attachment. If chains are used as attachments, and they are loose near the belt, use an additional carabiner to pull them together.

A safety-first, heavy-duty set-up for the hip-belt squat.

Safety is paramount. Whatever belt and attachments you use, they must not fail you. They must be strong enough to hold the weight. And all carabiners must be heavy duty, and secure. There must be no risk of them opening during a set.

Rest the belt on your hip bones and upper buttocks. Don't cinch it around your waist. Experiment to find the most comfortable position for you. Depending on the belt, and the attachments, you may need to use padding such as a folded towel between the belt and your hips, and perhaps between the chains or straps and your body, too.

Place the platforms next to a power rack, or a stable, stationary object that's secured to the floor. Space the platforms so that there's just room for a 35-pound or 15-kilo plate on a loading pin to travel up and down without striking the platforms. To accommodate a larger plate you would need to use a wider stance—perhaps too wide. This wouldn't be necessary unless you had a full stack of 35-pounders and needed to use 45-pounders. Another alternative would be continued use of the smaller plates but with a taller loading pin, and taller platforms.

As an alternative to the loading pin, at least to begin with, you could suspend plates or a dumbbell directly from your belt.

You'll be tethered to the rack or other stationary object, so it must be steadfast. If the rack isn't fixed to the floor, load it with sufficient weight on the opposite side to you, so that it can't topple when pulled. Alternatively, have someone pull on the opposite side to you, for counterbalance. There must be *no chance* of the rack (or other stationary object) moving while you hip-belt squat, *or* of your feet slipping.

A simple, introductory set-up for the hip-belt squat, using a belt designed for applying resistance for the parallel bar dip, and a strong band. The band should be looped around the hands before being grasped in the hands. A slight hollow should be maintained in the lower back at all times. The far right photograph shows some rounding of the lower back—avoid this.

Loop a strong length of towing strap or rope securely around the rack or other stable object, at about the height of your hips when you're standing on the platforms, or lower if the attachment point on the rack is further than about four feet or one meter from the platforms. There must be no risk of the strap snapping, or slipping out of position.

If the strap is fixed on the support at chest height or higher, it will probably lead to your torso leaning forward during the descent.

Strap may be preferable to rope, because the latter may cut into your skin. Alternatively, use rope and wear gloves. You'll need about five meters if you loop the strap around the posts of a rack. The ends of the strap must be within easy reach when you're on the platforms.

Wrap the ends of the strap or rope snugly around your hands next to your thumbs rather than around the knuckles at the base of your fingers. Grip the ends securely, so that when you stand on the platforms your elbows are almost straight, and the strap is taut. There must be no chance of losing your grip.

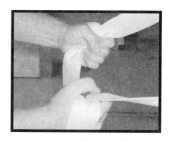

The loading pin should be placed on a sturdy crate or box that's temporarily positioned on the floor between your feet. The pin is loaded while on the crate or box. The loading pin needs to be elevated so that you don't have to squat down far to attach your belt to the loading pin.

Performance

Without a belt or weight, familiarize yourself with the exercise. Stand with the towing strap around your hands and pulled taut, elbows

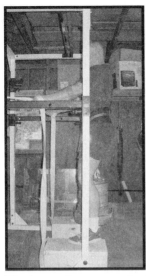

The heavy-duty set-up for the hip-belt squat. Regardless of the type of belt used, note the position of the torso with respect to the rack uprights. The torso must move down and back, not merely down.

straight or slightly bent, heels hip-width or a little wider, and each foot flared about 30 degrees. Reposition the platforms if need be.

Keep your torso vertical, head up, eyes forward, shoulders retracted, and lower back slightly hollowed. As you descend, *move your torso and hips to the rear*, allow but minimize forward travel of your knees, and keep your back vertical.

If the strap is too short, or the platforms are too far from the rack, you'll lean forward as you descend. If you lean forward, your lower back will round earlier than it would otherwise, which would reduce the safe range of motion for your thighs. Keep your torso vertical. Configure the set-up accordingly.

Take about three seconds for the descent. Descend as low as is safe for your knees and back—ideally to below the point where your upper thighs are parallel with the floor. Pause for a moment, stay tight, then smoothly ascend to the starting position—push only through your heels. Pushing only through your heels minimizes the stress on your knees. Take about three seconds for each ascent. At the top of each rep, either gently straighten your knees fully, or keep them slightly bent. Pause for a second at the top, then descend into the next rep.

During each rep, don't tug on the towing strap, or bend your elbows more than just slightly. The purpose of the strap is to help you to avoid forward lean of your torso, and minimize forward lean of your shins.

Perform several reps, then try a slightly wider stance, and different degrees of toe flare, to find what feels most comfortable for you. And experiment with the length of the strap, to find what works best.

When you're familiar with the exercise, try it with a belt and one plate on the loading pin. Load the pin while it's on the crate. Then grab the towing strap and stand in position on the platforms. Dip the short distance required to connect the attachment(s) from your belt to the loading pin, using a carabiner. Now, pull your shoulders back, slightly hollow your lower back, and stand. When the weight is significant, push your hands on your thighs to help you safely into the starting, upright position. Then get an assistant to move the crate away. While standing upright on the platforms, loop the strap around your hands until it's taut, and get set for your first rep.

As you descend, the plates should move down *and* to the rear, as should your hips and torso.

Although there's no compression on your back from the hip-belt squat, still keep your back slightly hollowed, for safety. *Never round your back, flatten your back, or slump forward.* If you can't maintain the right positioning, you may be holding a strap that's too short, and you may be descending too far. Adjust the length of attachment between your belt and the loading pin so that at your bottom position the resistance is about an inch above the floor, and you're about two inches above the point at which your lower back would start to round.

Get the feedback from an assistant, who should assess you from the side view, to help you to find the right set-up configuration, and to master the performance of the exercise.

Finish each set in the standing, upright position. Then get an assistant to reposition the crate. Set the weight on the crate, release the belt, stand and then rest in order to get ready for any subsequent set.

Don't set the resistance on the floor between reps. If, however, you get stuck on the ascent, descend further than normal, set the weight on the floor, and release the belt. For the next set, reposition the crate under the weight. Strip the loading pin before repositioning it on the crate, and reloading it. But, as much as possible, avoid failing on a rep like this, because releasing the belt is awkward when you're in a full squat, as is getting off the platforms. Both may irritate your knees.

The orthodox breathing pattern when squatting is to take one or more deep breaths while standing, descend, and then exhale during the ascent. Alternatively, breathe freely.

Once you know your set-up configuration, be consistent. Always put the platforms the same distance from the rack and same space apart, place the belt around your hips in the same position, use the same attachments between the belt and loading pin, use the same tethering strap and fasten it to the rack at the same height, grip the strap the same distance from the rack, loop it the same number of times around your hands, and so on.

If you've tried the technique as described, started very light with low intensity, and built up the poundage and intensity gradually, but *still* experienced knee irritation, try modifications. Wait until the knee irritation has healed, then reduce the range of motion so that your upper thighs don't descend further than where they are parallel with the floor. If that doesn't correct the problem, adjust the technique further while still not descending beyond the parallel position. When your shins are vertical, or almost vertical, there may be excessive stress on your knees. If a little more forward lean of your shins is allowed, that may increase involvement of your hip musculature, and hamstrings, and perhaps reduce stress on your knees. Try it with a reduced poundage to see if it's safe for you. If it is, try it with a greater range of motion, too.

Find the greatest, safe range of motion for you, and then gradually build up the poundage.

Especially for men, wear elasticated, giving briefs and shorts (or tracksuit bottoms) while performing the hip-belt squat, or otherwise the tension of the attachments against the clothing around your groin area may produce excessive discomfort.

It may require several workouts of experimentation before you find the hip-belt squat set-up and performance that works best for you. And initially you may find that your lower-back and hip musculature tires quickly once resistance is loaded. Be patient but persistent while you familiarize yourself with the exercise, and adapt to it. The hip-belt squat has the potential to be a safe, highly effective exercise, and especially valuable if you can't safely back squat, front squat, parallel-grip deadlift, or leg press. It's worth the time investment required to master it.

The hip-belt squat described here is based on that reported in the article "Safe and Heavy Hip-Belt Squats," by Nathan Harvey, published in HARDGAINER *issue #89. Nathan reported the methods of Ed Komoszewski. Photographs from that article have been reprinted here.*

25. TIMED HOLD

Main muscles worked

finger flexion muscles, forearms

Capsule description

hold a bar next to your thighs while you stand with straight knees

For best effect, use a bar that's thicker than usual. A standard bar of an inch, or slightly thicker, will work your grip hard and do a good job, but a thick bar will do a better job. A small increase in diameter produces a substantial change in girth, and a big increase in the difficulty of handling the bar.

If there's no thick bar where you train, improvise. At the minimum, wrap something around a bar to mimic a thick bar. Use the same modification each time you do the exercise.

Encourage the management of where you train to buy a ready-made thick bar. Alternatively, a local metal worker could make one to order. It will be a terrific addition to the gym and won't be expensive unless it's a solid, chromed bar.

Comparison of a regular-diameter barbell, and a two-inch diameter one.

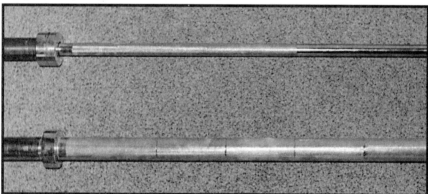

Set-up and positioning

Load a bar on boxes, or set it on the pins in a power rack, or across the safety bars in a squat rack, so that you have only to pull it up two inches before holding it in a standing position. You'll need to lower it only two inches once your grip has given out at the end of the hold. In effect, you hold the lockout position of the deadlift.

In a power rack getting into position for the timed hold, using a thick bar. The pin position should be higher than shown here, to make it easier to get the bar into the starting position.

Performance

Start with clean, dry hands and bar, and apply chalk or rosin to your fingers, palms, and the inside area of your thumbs and index fingers. Take a pronated grip on the bar a little wider than hip width, and keep the back of each hand in a straight line with its forearm. Then bend your knees a little, pull your shoulders back, hollow your lower back slightly, and stand upright.

While standing, keep your knees straight, shoulders retracted, and torso vertical or tilted forward slightly. Never round your back. The bar can be pressed against your thighs, but don't bend your knees or lean backward or otherwise you'll cheat through taking some of the weight on your thighs. Furthermore, leaning backward while supporting a load is harmful for the spine.

During the second half of each timed hold, don't merely grasp the bar. Try to crush it. Just holding the bar isn't the way to get the most staying power out of your grip. Squeeze the bar as hard as possible. Then when your grip is close to failing, try to bend the bar. Although you can't bend it, attempting to can extend the life of your grip. Shrugging your shoulders a little, and keeping your elbows slightly bent, may also help you to get more mileage out of your grip.

Don't be concerned about when to breathe during thick-bar holds—breathe freely. Don't hold your breath.

Select a duration for the holds. Between 30 and 60 seconds will probably suit most trainees. Settle on a specific number of seconds. Once you can hold the bar for that time, add a little weight next session.

Supplementary exercises

When I wrote BUILD MUSCLE, LOSE FAT, LOOK GREAT, I wanted to produce a complete book on exercise and physique transformation, so it had to include exercise technique. I took most of the text from the second edition of THE INSIDER'S TELL-ALL HANDBOOK ON WEIGHT-TRAINING TECHNIQUE, revised it and added many exercises, and produced Chapter 12 of BUILD MUSCLE. Then I took INSIDER'S out of print.

But then, in response to demand once again for a book on exercise technique alone, I took Chapter 12 from BUILD MUSCLE, LOSE FAT, LOOK GREAT, added some supplementary exercises and other additional material, and produced what you have here—the third edition of INSIDER'S.

But BUILD MUSCLE, LOSE FAT, LOOK GREAT includes about 400 pages on topics *other than* exercise technique.

REMINDERS . . .
Fundamentals of correct exercise technique

1. Before you can apply correct exercise technique, you first need to know what correct exercise technique is. Study this book carefully.

2. Before a set, review the correct exercise technique.

3. Never rush into a set, grab the bar and then realize after the first rep that you took an imbalanced grip, the wrong stance, or are lopsided while on a bench. Get correctly positioned for every set.

4. Be 100% focused and attentive while you train.

5. Lift the weight, don't throw it; and lower it, don't drop it. Use control at all times. Move the resistance *smoothly*, without any sudden, or explosive movements.

6. Most trainees use more weight than they can handle correctly. This leads to cheating, loss of control, and produces injury sooner or later.

26. GRIP MACHINE TRAINING

Main muscles worked

forearms, finger muscles

Capsule description

close a moveable bar to a fixed upper bar by using only your fingers

A good grip machine is more comfortable, adjustable (for accommodating individual hand sizes, and changing resistance), and effective at developing crushing strength than are fixed-strength grippers. Grippers that are adjustable are much closer to the versatility of a grip machine. Fixed-resistance grippers can be fun to use, but depending on your hand size and strength they may be uncomfortable and awkward, and perhaps favor one hand more than the other, depending on the design.

While using a proper grip machine is the ideal, it's not a necessity. A grip machine can be simulated using a power rack. Set the two pairs of pins in the rack so that, with a bar set upon each pair, the space between the two levels of pins is right for squeezing the lower bar from extended fingers until it touches the top pins. If the distance is too great—and the next pin setting makes it too little—then, in the "too great" setting, fix something on the lower pins so that the lower bar starts from the correct position. Moving the lower bar up and down against the rack's uprights will help you to keep the bar in the right groove. The bar resting on the upper pins should not be so long that it gets in the way of the plates loaded on the lower bar. Get in a power rack and see how you can make this method work.

A better mock-up needs a special bar with hooks, as illustrated. Any metal worker could easily make such a bar.

Regardless of whether you use a grip machine or a mock-up, use it only for your gripping muscles. When the weight is very demanding, the exercise can become more of a shrug from the trapezius than a squeeze from the grip. Keep your hands fixed to the top of the unit during the exercise. If your hands rise off the top bar, you've started to assist your grip by shrugging the weight. Avoid this. Doing the exercise while seated helps ensure strict form and keeps the target muscles involved to the full. And be consistent with how you position your feet—braced or unbraced.

The grip machine is typically used with the thumbs around the top, and the other digits doing the movement. The exercise can also be done with the thumbs on the bottom, while seated or kneeling. This is a weaker squeezing position because the thumbs alone have to do the work. Finish off each grip machine session with a set of thumbs-below work, to ensure that all five digits of each hand are worked.

Thumbs-down work.

Two mock-ups for a grip machine. The bottom one requires a bar with hooks.

27. LEVER BAR WORK

Main muscles worked

forearms

Capsule description

with your elbow straight, lift a bar by moving at your wrist (and, perhaps, at your shoulder, too)

First are the two basic movements shown on the next page. Take a dumbbell rod and load only one end with a few pounds. With your arm hanging vertically by your side, and elbow straight, hold the unweighted end. With the weighted end to the front, move the rod up and down by moving at your wrist only. Don't bend your elbow, or move at your shoulder. Do maximum reps to the front, and then do the same with the other hand. Then repeat but with the weighted end to the rear. The second action is stronger than the first, so you'll be able to do more reps to the rear when using the same weight. Alternatively, use a heavier weight for the stronger action, and target the same rep count for both movements.

You don't have to use a dumbbell rod or a purpose-made lever bar. You could use a cricket or baseball bat, a sledge hammer, or a broomstick with a broom attached. If you can't handle the whole length of the fixed-weight item with one hand, grip it down the length a little and, over time, progress to the end. As an alternative you could use both hands and hold the item at its full length. Progress to exercising each hand separately once you've developed sufficient strength from training with both hands together.

There are many variations of the two basic lever bar movements. You don't have to do the exercise while standing. You could, for example, kneel and pick up the lever tool from the floor in front of you. Raise it until your arm is parallel to the floor, keeping your elbow straight and the lever bar parallel to the floor. From the front, use one hand at a time, or both hands together. With the lever bar behind you, you could squat down, take the bar, and stand while keeping the bar parallel to the floor and your lifting arm vertical, and elbow straight. Or, you could take the bar from a bench rather than the floor. Use your imagination and you'll find a number of ways to work your forearms and wrists to their limit with a lever bar.

Lever bar work where you raise your arm in front until it's parallel to the floor is very demanding on your elbow and wrist. Take several weeks of gradually increasing resistance and intensity before you start to train with maximum effort. If you rush into intensive lever bar work, especially the type that keeps your arm parallel to the floor, you're likely to injure yourself. Lever bar work with a vertical arm is safer.

Small discs—those lighter than 2.5 pounds or 1.25 kilos—have great value for all exercises. But for exercises that don't have a big poundage potential, like lever bar movements, little discs are essential. Without them you'll be unable to apply a gradual increase in resistance.

An example of lever bar work, using a dumbbell rod loaded at one end

An example of lever bar work to the rear.

28. OVERHEAD LOCKOUT

Main muscles worked

deltoids, triceps, trapezius

Capsule description

seated, with arms overhead, move the bar up and down a few inches

To focus a lot of work on the lateral head of the deltoids while using a big exercise, use the partial overhead press—just the top three to four inches. This works more than just the lateral head of the deltoids. The whole of the shoulder-cap muscle is involved. Use this exercise as an alternative to the full-range overhead press.

Set-up and positioning

Set up an adjustable incline bench inside a power rack, or a Smith machine. Be sure that the bench is sturdy, heavy and stable. Set it up so that the angle between the horizontal and the back of the upright part of the bench is 75 to 80 degrees. If the seat is adjustable, set it at the position next to horizontal so that you're less likely to slide out of position during a set.

Place the bench so that your eyes, when your shoulders and head are against the bench, are a little in front of the barbell as it rests on the pins and against the front or rear uprights of a power rack. This assumes that you use the type of power rack that enables you to set a bench inside it in the position required. The rack's uprights should be behind the bar as you look at the bar while you're in position against the back support. Alternatively, your eyes could be a little in front of the bar of a Smith machine. Exactly where your eyes will be, relative to the bar, will be determined by factors including the angle of the back support of the bench, your arm length, and how much your head is tilted. Find the best positioning for you.

The bar must be set at a height only three to four inches below the position where it would be if your elbows were fully locked out overhead. Position the pins of a power rack appropriately for you, and then load your bar while it's across the pins, not while it's on the weight saddles. This will be your starting position. Never take the bar out of the saddles of a power rack and do the exercise without pins set in place. That would leave you with nothing to catch the bar if you failed on a rep.

Chalk your hands before each work set, to prevent your hands slipping on the bar. Use a shoulder-width grip, never a wide grip. But if your grip is too close, you'll easily lose balance of the barbell.

In a power rack the bar should, preferably, travel up and down against the uprights. This keeps you in the right groove. If you're doing the exercise in a Smith machine, the bar will already be locked into position.

With a Smith machine it's critical that you can safely rack the bar. At the end of a set your shoulders and arms will be very fatigued, and you'll not have full control over the bar. Set up the machine so that your bottom position is where the latches are at rest. Keep the latches inside the guided pathway during each set. Then you'll be able to move the bar up and down the guided pathway without ever twisting your wrists to take the latches out. Then, even if you lose control, the bar will come to rest safely. This is possible only because the lockout is a partial movement.

Overhead lockout in a power rack. Whether using a power rack, or a Smith machine, your arms should be in a vertical or near-vertical plane throughout the exercise—not at the same 75 to 80 degrees of the bench. Arrange your setup position accordingly.

The overhead lockout can be done without the vertical guide of the rack uprights, or a Smith machine. But still use a power rack, with pins set in the same position as for the guided style. If done with insufficient control in the unguided style, there's a greatly increased risk of injury because the bar can easily move out of the right groove due to one hand getting in front of the other. This causes dangerous asymmetrical stress. If you can't keep control over the bar in the unguided style, use only the guided pathway method.

Performance

Don't do the reps in a non-stop touch-and-go style because that's an easy way to lose the horizontal balance of the bar, and stress one shoulder more than the other. This can cause injuries. Very briefly set the bar on the pins between reps so that you can keep in the groove more easily.

Do the reps with control. Don't blast the bar off the pins, because that will cause you to lose the groove. It will also make you slam into the locked-out position, which is harmful for your elbows. And the excessive momentum will take some of the stress away from the primary target muscles—the deltoids.

As you do the lockouts, you may want to let your head come forward slightly so that the bar is moving up and down behind your head.

After your final rep, with your arms fully locked out, shrug your shoulders up (and hence raise your arms). Though the bar will move only an inch or so, the shrug will add further stress to your deltoids. Do as many overhead shrugs as possible.

A harder method is to shrug at the top of each rep. To optimize this style, set up two pairs of pins four inches apart. Arrange the height of the pins in the rack so that the first three inches of the movement completes the lockout. The final inch is for the shrug only. You must not be able to lock out for the entire four inches. For each rep you must lock out *and* shrug in order to be able to touch the bar to the upper pair of pins, with the barbell sliding up and down against the rack's uprights.

Warm up well, practice the groove with a light weight, and then carefully build up the weight from workout to workout. Poundage potential is influenced by factors including the range of motion you use, and whether you shrug on each rep or just at the end of each set.

During this exercise, don't exaggerate the arch in your lower back.

Spotting

The correct groove can be lost easily, especially if the exercise is not done using a guided pathway. The spotter should look out for the bar tipping, one hand getting forward of the other, or the bar being pressed off center, and provide help to prevent serious form deterioration.

Using a Smith machine, a spotter is essential unless you never take the latches out of the guided pathway. At the end of a hard set, if you have moved the latches forward, you may have trouble putting them back in the locked position. When fatigued at the end of a hard set, it's easy to lose control of the movement. A spotter would then be critical, to ensure that you don't lose control over the bar.

The Smith machine has few uses for safe training. The overhead lockout, because it uses a short range of motion, is one of the safe applications if it's done as described here. But don't do any type of full-range press in the Smith machine. The rigid vertical pathway of this machine is unnatural to the body for full-range pressing. It will set you up for chronic injuries.

29. PINCH-GRIP LIFTING

Main muscles worked

forearms, finger muscles

Capsule description

lift resistance while holding it with only your pinch-grip strength

Lifting using your pinch-grip strength is one of the best grip, forearm and finger exercises. Never mind that you may never have seen anyone do it. There are many terrific exercises that are unheard of in most gyms.

Set-up and positioning

If you don't have a purpose-built pinch-grip device, rig up something that does the job. Get a 2 x 4-inch block of wood about 24 inches long, for pinching across the 2-inch width, and bore a hole through its center. (Use a 2 x 5-inch block if you have huge hands.) Pass a strong cord through the hole, and suspend a loading pin with plates on it, or an adjustable dumbbell. With a longer board you could have a large hook securely fixed near to each end, on the underside. The board could then be hooked around a regular barbell. By lifting the pinch board, the barbell will be lifted off the floor. The longer board is needed to reduce the problems with balance that can arise when the device is hooked up to a barbell.

You could get a welder to produce a pinch block for you out of metal. Have matt paint put on it to help reduce the likelihood of slippage.

A 2-inch thickness is a good standard, but you could use a slightly thicker or thinner thickness if you prefer. If the gripping surface is too smooth, fix it for easier gripping by securely affixing some rough material such as canvas.

Another equipment alternative is to fix a couple of plates, smooth sides out, to a metal or wooden rod. Fix them together with collars. This becomes your gripping site. Outside the inside collars, load plates as you need them, with further collars used to hold the plates in place.

To protect your feet, stand the weight on a low platform. This will keep the resistance above your feet. Put some rubber matting or thick cardboard under the weights in case you drop the pinch-grip device. Keep your feet well to the sides of the area that the weights move above. To help in this respect, avoid using full-size weight plates—stick to small- and medium-diameter plates. Be safety conscious.

An easily-made and adjustable pinch- grip device using a 2-inch wooden rod.

Pinch-grip sliver bar

To train your finger-tip pinching strength, rather than that of your entire fingers, get a thin but strong flat piece of wood and find a way to suspend weight from it. Or, get a metal worker to weld a piece of 10 x 1-inch flat bar to a hook. Then attach the hook to a loading pin. Pinch grip the sliver bar with both hands, or with one at a time. Put your thumb(s) on one side and your other digits on the other side. Find a specific grip and site on the bar you're comfortable with, make a written note of it if necessary, and use the same grip each time you use the sliver bar.

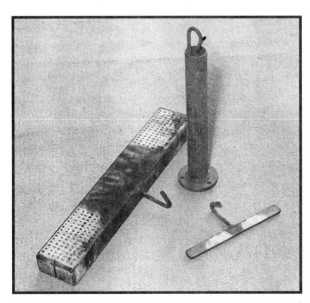

A 2 x 4 x 22-inch metal pinch-grip block, loading pin, and sliver bar.

Using the sliver bar, in addition to the grip that involves all of your digits, you can exercise any pair of a thumb and one finger from the same hand. You can use this piece of equipment to mimic pinching a coin attached to resistance.

Performance

Regardless of which pinch-grip device you use, do reps, singles, or timed holds. You can train one hand at a time, or both together.

With the pinch block, and for each hand, put the full length of your four adjacent fingers down one side of the block, and the length of your thumb down the other side. Grip with the entire length of all your digits, not just the tips. Find the most comfortable and secure gripping site for you, and stick with it. Use the identical way of gripping your device each time you use it.

When pinch-grip lifting an item from the floor, don't snatch at it. To reduce the chance of the object slipping out of your fingers—even a weight you know you have the strength to handle—squeeze hard and then *ease* it off the floor.

Pinch lifting for timed holds is easier if your hands are held against your thighs rather than out away from them. Be consistent in the form you use, or use both styles. Use more weight in the against-the-thighs style, or hold the same weight for more time.

When your grip is close to failing in any pinch-grip work, make a deliberate effort to try to bend whatever you're holding. While you can't bend it, the attempt to can extend the life of your grip. And don't just try to hold the pinch-grip device, try to *crush* it.

Keep accurate records of the weights you lift and the style(s) you use. If you use the against-the-thighs style, keep your legs locked and your torso either vertical or tilted forward slightly. If you bend your thighs and/or lean back as you do the pinch-grip lifting, you'll cheat because the weight will be partly supported on your thighs, thus defeating the object of the exercise. If you always keep your hands off your thighs, you'll eliminate this problem.

Three pinch-grip devices in use: two plates locked together, smooth sides out (left); 2 x 4-inch block (middle), and sliver bar.

30. RADER CHEST PULL

Main structure worked

rib cage

This exercise was developed by Peary Rader, 1909 to 1991, who was one of the most influential figures in the Iron Game. Among his many contributions, Rader founded IRON MAN *magazine, in 1936. He remained owner and publisher until he sold the magazine in 1986. (It was Peary who, in the 1980s, published Stuart's first articles, and gave him his start as a writer.)*

This is another stretching and forced breathing exercise, which, like the breathing pullover, may enlarge your rib cage, deepen your chest, and help improve your posture. It may be especially effective for teenagers, and trainees in their early twenties, but is worth a try at any age. There's no science to confirm this, however. I believe the Rader chest pull helped me, and other people have reported benefits, too. Especially when I was a teenager, I used the breathing pullover and the Rader chest pull.

Stand at about arm's length from a vertical bar, with your feet hip-width apart. Alternatively, use a sturdy, stable object that can be grasped at about head height. An upright on a power rack, or a door jamb, will do the job. If you use an upright of a power rack, or a vertical bar, keep your hands together. If you use another object, keep your hands close together.

While keeping your arms straight, take a deep breath and simultaneously pull down *and in* with your arms. Don't contract your abdominal muscles. Keep them relaxed. If you tense your abs, this will flatten your chest and defeat the purpose of the exercise. Done correctly, the Rader chest pull will raise your chest and produce a pull and slight discomfort in your sternum. If you don't feel this, you're not doing the exercise properly.

You may get a better effect if you bend your arms *slightly*, because this will let you pull harder. The harder you pull, the better the effect on your rib cage, so long as you're pulling in the right way.

Rader recommended that you tense the muscles at the front of your neck and then pull your head back. This should be done at the same time as you pull down *and in* with your arms. This neck involvement provides further stretching and lifting of your rib cage. But don't apply this tip until after you've learned to apply the other instruction.

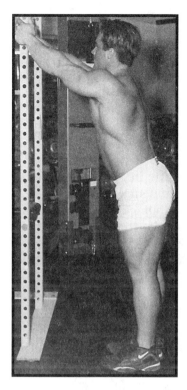

Starting position of the Rader chest pull.

Once you get to grips with it you'll feel a considerable stretch in your rib cage. It may take a while to get the exercise right. You may have to fine-tune the height you place your hands, the spacing between your hands, the distance between your feet and the base of the object you hold, and the angle of pull you use. Persist until you get it right.

Hold your breath for as long as comfortable, and throughout the entire time you should be able to feel the pull and slight discomfort in your sternum. Don't, however, hold your breath until you're almost ready to burst, because you need to be able to perform up to 20 reps for a single set. How long you can comfortably hold your breath will depend on the state of your breathing prior to performing the chest pull, and your general conditioning. With practice, over time, you'll be able to hold each pull for a longer time, for a comparable level of discomfort. Somewhere in the range of four to six seconds per pull will be fine.

You can perform the Rader chest pull after an exercise that gets you heavily winded, or when you're not winded. As with the breathing pullover, rib cage work can be done much more frequently than other weight-training exercises. It's not high-intensity systemically-demanding work.

Go easy to begin with, especially if you're not doing the Rader chest pull when winded. The forced and exaggerated breathing may make you feel dizzy unless you work into it over a few weeks. Your chest may get very sore, too, if you don't work into the exercise gradually. Exercise caution and good sense.

31. WRIST ROLLER TRAINING

Main muscles worked

forearms

Capsule description

with cord, attach a weight to a handle; roll the resistance up and down

The wrist roller is a classic grip and forearm developer, although it's rarely performed in gyms today. Its equipment needs are simple. You can make yourself a wrist roller to use at home if where you train doesn't have one. When using a thick handle you don't need much weight, and you can improvise for resistance if you don't have weight plates at home. Alternatively, you could take your own wrist roller to the gym with you.

Set-up and positioning

Make a wrist roller by getting a smooth, wooden rod at least 18 inches long and between 2 and 2.5 inches in diameter. You could also use a length of pipe. While you could use a thinner rod, a thicker one will train your grip, hands and forearms more effectively. Drill a vertical hole through the center and securely tie a piece of strong cord through the hole. At least initially, try a cord about 40 to 45 inches long. Securely attach a hook or carabiner to the dangling end of the cord. Then hook it onto the loading pin that holds the weight plates. If you use another loading system, make sure it's secure.

Hold the handle with both hands, knuckles on top. Use a grip spacing that feels most comfortable for you. This exercise is usually done with a close grip. This is a necessity in most cases because wrist roller handles are usually too short. But with a handle at least 18 inches long you can choose between a close- or medium-width grip.

Wrist roller training can be done with an underhand grip, but this is awkward and less effective than an overhand grip. If you want to try an underhand grip, use a shoulder-width one rather than a close grip. The description that follows concerns the knuckles-on-top grip.

Don't keep your arms out straight in front of you. Done straight out in front, you may end up suffering from more fatigue in your shoulders than in your grip. The point is to train your forearms to the fullest, so keep them hanging (with bent elbows) in the vertical plane, and focus on your grip and forearms.

Wrist roller in use.

Stand on a pair of sturdy, stable boxes, benches or chairs. If you do the wrist rolling while standing on the floor, you'll not have much space in which to do the exercise while keeping your arms hanging in the vertical plane. You would have hardly any range of movement.

Another problem with wrist rolling while standing on the floor comes from the resistance moving around at the bottom of the exercise. This puts your shins and feet at risk of injury.

Space the boxes, benches or chairs so there's plenty of room for the resistance to move in as you do the exercise. Then, even on the final rep of the exercise, when you're having a wrestle to get the weight up, you'll not risk hitting your legs or feet. Your legs and feet will be out of the way. Then you can concentrate on the exercise. And use small and medium-diameter plates so that there's less potential for the resistance striking whatever you stand on.

The taller the objects upon which you stand, and the shorter the loading pin you employ, the longer the cord you can use without the weights hitting the floor at the bottom of each rep. Tailor the cord's length according to your own circumstances.

Put something on the floor to protect it in case the handle slips out of your hands and the resistance crashes to the floor.

Performance

Along with sheer holding strength, there are two actions involved in this exercise: wrist extension, and wrist flexion. In extension, the knuckles are raised; and in flexion, the knuckles are lowered. A different set of muscles is involved in each action. Because your extension and flexion strengths are not the same, doing the exercise with the same weight for both actions means that you'll need more reps for one action than the other to produce a comparable degree of work. Alternatively, use more weight for the stronger action.

Focus on flexion first. With the cord extended and the weight hanging just above the floor, and using a knuckles-up grip, roll the weight up by turning each hand alternately. Your knuckles on a given hand should move downward while that hand turns on the handle to roll the weight up a little. The cord will hang on the side of the handle nearest to your body. When the cord is fully rolled up, immediately unroll it by moving your wrists the other way, through extension. Don't rest at the top.

While the downward movement of the weight involves the extension muscles, that involvement is much less severe than that on the flexion muscles while raising the weight. Gravity helps on the descent, but hinders on the ascent. Don't rest at the bottom Keep the exercise moving until your grip and forearms are exhausted.

Rest at least a few minutes. Then repeat the exercise but this time reverse the movement. This is the second wrist rolling action. Start with the cord extended and the weight just above the floor. Use extension to raise the weight, and flexion to lower it. This means that the cord will hang on the far side of the handle.

Other tips for wrist rolling

The second wrist rolling action will suffer due to fatigue from the first action. Because of this you'll probably want to rest longer than a few minutes between doing the two sets. If you do this exercise at home you can do the two actions at different times of the day, or on different days.

As far as weights and record keeping go, you have two options. First, use the same weight for both actions, and max out on reps in both cases and be content with a different rep count for each. The other option is to use more weight for the stronger action. Determine your strength difference between the two actions. Then you can target the same rep count for each action, but use a different weight for each. This assumes a consistent rest period between whenever you perform the two actions. If you vary the rest period, that will affect the strength difference and ruin record keeping consistency. Be consistent with how and when you do the two wrist rolling actions.

When rolling the cord around the handle, avoid getting your fingers caught in your clothing. Keep your shirt tucked in your shorts or tracksuit bottom, and the handle of the wrist roller a few inches away from your thighs.

You may have a tendency to favor your stronger hand, and move the handle more on each turn with that hand than the other. Avoid that. Make a deliberate effort to involve both hands equally, on the ascent *and* descent of the exercise.

A little chalk on your hands may help, depending on the surface of the handle you use. Experiment to find how much works best for you.

Because the wrist roller with a thick handle doesn't have a big poundage potential, small discs are vital for applying progressive resistance gradually.

A fixed-weight dumbbell could be suspended from the cord, rather than plates on a loading pin, but inch your way from one dumbbell size to the next. Don't, for example, make a single five-pound jump from a 40-pound dumbbell to a 45-pound one. Instead, by attaching small discs to the 40-pound dumbbell, progress a quarter- or a half-pound at a time. But instead of a dumbbell and additional separate plates, or plates on a loading pin, you could attach the cord to a plates directly.

PART 3

How to handle weights between exercises 274
How to compose exercise technique checklists 280
Video recordings 282
How to become flexible 288

About the author 308

I promote a conservative approach to training. Experience from more than 30 years—from my own personal training, and from observing countless other trainees—has taught me that the conservative approach isn't just the safest way, *it's also the most effective way over the long term.*

How to handle weights between exercises

Correct lifting technique isn't restricted to exercises. It's also needed while setting up an exercise, or putting equipment away. Many trainees have been injured through improper weight handling between exercises.

Plate handling

With a large plate, carry it by itself in two hands, held tightly to your abdomen or chest. When putting the plate on a bar, plate stand, or rack, or when taking it from a bar, plate stand, or rack, get as close as possible, feet side-by-side, plate close to and centered on your torso, head up, shoulders pulled back, and your lower back slightly hollowed. Never round your shoulders as you handle any load.

If you return a heavy plate to a plate stand using one hand only— perhaps in a confined place—keep the plate close to you, and brace your other hand on the stand.

Don't carry two or more stacked plates. When carrying two plates, hold one in each hand, for symmetrical distribution of load. Never struggle with multiple large plates—carry them one at a time. The additional time you need to make multiple visits to a bar, stand, or rack is a small price to pay for safety.

If there's a selection of plates, choose those that have a deep, outer ridge or lip. That construction is easier to hold than that of smooth-sided plates, or ones with only a shallow outer ridge.

If you ever drop a plate, immediately get your feet out of the way. Feet have been broken by dropped plates.

Barbell handling

Strip a bar of any plates, before moving it. The bar may, however, be a fixed-weight one, which you can't strip down. The heavier the weight, the greater the care required. But even light weights need care. When taking a bar from or returning it to stands, or anywhere else, keep it close to your body, get your feet as close as possible to it, bend at your knees, keep your head up, and lower back slightly hollowed.

Dumbbell handling

When lifting dumbbells from a rack, get as close as possible to them. Bend your knees, keep your head up, and your lower back slightly hollowed. Lift two dumbbells simultaneously and symmetrically, or one at a time (with both hands on the handle) but symmetrically. With two dumbbells, the load will be symmetrical provided the 'bells are lifted at the same time, your feet are side-by-side, and the weights are equidistant from your midline. If one foot is in front of the other, for example, stress will be applied asymmetrically, and the risk of injury will be increased.

An alternative way of handling a single dumbbell is to get close to the rack, with knees bent and lower back slightly hollowed, grab the dumbbell with one hand, and brace the other hand on the rack or another dumbbell. As you lift the dumbbell, simultaneously push hard with your bracing hand, to maintain symmetrical distribution of stress. Once you're standing, hold the dumbbell symmetrically in front of your thighs, with both hands, and then carry it to position. Return for the second dumbbell, if required.

When taking a dumbbell off the floor, take special care. This involves a greater range of motion than taking the weight from an elevated surface, and easily leads to rounding of the back. With your feet side-by-side about shoulder-width apart, and astride the dumbbell, bend at your knees, keep your head up, and your lower back slightly hollowed. Grab the dumbbell with your left hand, for example, and place your right hand on your right thigh. As you lift the dumbbell, simultaneously push hard with your right hand, for symmetrical distribution of stress. Once you're standing, hold the dumbbell symmetrically in front of your thighs, with both hands, and then carry it away. Return for the second dumbbell, if required.

Between sets, to reduce dumbbell handling awkwardness, set the 'bells on a bench, box, or other elevated surface, rather than the floor.

incorrect

correct

Weight plates with a deep, outer ridge, or lip (left), permit easier handling than plates with a shallow outer ridge (right).

incorrect

correct

Plate handling on a loading pin

The hip-belt squat, pinch-grip lifting, and wrist roller require the use of a loading pin.

The longer the loading pin, the more space there is for stacking plates. When plates of the same size are loaded consecutively, especially large ones, it's easy to trap your fingers, and tricky to remove the plates. To make loading safer and easier, place a small plate between each pair of large plates. This will, however, use up more of the loading pin than would stacking the same number of large plates directly on top of each other, and thus a taller loading pin may be required sooner. For the hip-belt squat, taller platforms may be required for standing on, to compensate for a taller loading pin, so that the range of motion of the exercise isn't reduced.

Respect your limitations

Don't try to lift something you know is beyond you. Get help.

A loading pin with one 15-kilo and four 20-kilo plates stacked on it, with a single 1-1/4 kilo plate between each pair of large plates, to produce a gap between the big discs. See text. The loading pin here is attached to a carabiner, which in turn is attached to the front strap of an IronMind® Enterprises' hip belt.

How to compose exercise technique checklists

When overhauling the technique of an exercise you're familiar with, or when learning a new exercise, there are many points to remember. To begin with you'll be unable to remember all of them. But with time you should be able to execute correct technique automatically.

Use a checklist for each exercise to remind you of the key points that are not yet embedded in your mind. Even an experienced trainee can develop bad habits, and would benefit from such a checklist.

Write a checklist for each exercise that needs it, on a separate card for each. But before you compose these lists, review the relevant sections in this book.

Use bold, clear writing on the cards. And keep the checklist brief. But each phrase or word will remind you of something to which you must pay special attention.

Review the relevant card prior to doing an exercise. Of course, don't read as you lift.

A spotter or training partner can be of tremendous value for giving you reminders of specific technique points. This can ensure that you don't break any of the points on your checklists. This applies to all rep counts, but perhaps especially to high-rep sets where concentration may be particularly challenging to sustain.

A reminder from a spotter or training partner may be all that you need to keep your technique on track. Not only will this keep your technique correct, it will help you to reach your rep target. Suppose, for example, you lose the right groove during a set of squats. This reduction of control will decrease your chances of making your rep target, but greatly increase the risk of injury.

As valuable as technique checklists are, however, they are no substitute for serious study of the detailed technique descriptions given in this book. And even after you've studied all of this book you'll need to revisit parts of it regularly. Review the technique of the exercises in each program you undertake, and apply correct technique to every exercise you use.

No one can remember everything. Everyone benefits from review work.

Video recordings: the acid test of correct exercise technique

The study of correct exercise technique is one thing, and vital. But being able to practice it is another matter. Proper use of a camcorder will help you to develop correct exercise technique. If you train alone at home with no one to check your technique, the camcorder can be an even greater blessing than it is for those who train among others.

Over a single year, most trainees will spend far more on unessential training-related items than the cost of a no-frills camcorder. Not only that, but most of those expenses will yield no positive return. A camcorder, used well, will teach you much about how to improve your exercise technique.

Consider a camcorder an investment for your training longevity and success. Invest in a camcorder before you spend on items that are, at best, of only marginal value.

While most people have the option to train in front of a mirror, this offers only a limited view for observing and monitoring exercise technique. While this is good enough for keeping a check on some small exercises, assuming you know what is and isn't correct technique, it's inadequate for most exercises, for reasons that include the following:

1. You can't carefully observe your technique while training hard.

2. Some exercises—for instance, the bench press—can't be reflected in a mirror for easy viewing.

3. Some exercises need to be seen from the side view—squat and deadlift, for example. While appropriate use of more than one mirror can let you see yourself from the side without having to turn your head, that's still not as useful as video recordings from the side.

4. A video recording is something you can keep and view repeatedly, if necessary, and use to compare with earlier or later recordings in order to monitor your technique thoroughly.

The first few times you view video recordings of your exercise technique may be eye openers. The lifting technique you think you use may not be what you actually use.

Using a camcorder

For video recordings of your training to have the potential to teach you much, you first need to know what constitutes the details of correct technique, and the errors to look out for. With that knowledge acquired from studying this book, record yourself from the side view of each exercise you do.

Have someone operate the camcorder while you exercise. Alternatively, mount the camcorder on a tripod and, for each exercise, set it at the appropriate height and position to record the full range of motion of the exercise.

In a commercial, college or other public gym, time the recording when the place is quiet; and preferably have someone operate the camcorder for you to avoid use of a tripod and having to set things up yourself. In a home gym there should be fewer logistical obstacles.

Study the recordings and set about correcting technique errors. Major errors may necessitate that you drop your poundages in the exercises concerned to little more than the bare bar. Learn the proper lifting technique, and then record and analyze your revised technique to check that you really are delivering what you think you're delivering. Then, if all's well, gradually build the weights back over a couple of months, or longer, with regular video taping to ensure that the new technique is maintained.

If the errors are small, you may need to reduce your poundages by only a little, and gradually build back the weights while maintaining correct technique.

When learning technique in major exercises, record yourself every workout for a few weeks. Then you can check that you're being consistent with the correct technique. Once the new grooves are embedded, you may only need to record yourself every few weeks.

When focusing on a specific detail of an exercise, it's critical that the camcorder is positioned at the right height. For example, if you're aiming to determine whether you're reaching or breaking parallel in the squat, you must have the camcorder positioned at about your knee height. If you have the camcorder at your standing eye level, you'll not get a true picture of the precise position of your thighs at the bottom of the descent.

To illustrate this, and while viewing from the side position, observe someone squatting while you're standing. Then get down on your knees and observe the same squatter from the low position. You'll probably see a noticeable difference between the two perceived depths. At powerlifting meets, squatting depth is observed from the low position, not while the judge is standing.

If you're trying to determine at what depth your lower back starts to round in the squat (but while using just the bare bar)—to discover the depth you should never get even close to with a heavy weight over your shoulders—you must have the camcorder set up at the height at about where the back rounding occurs.

If you squat in front of a mirror, what you may think is squatting to parallel may, in fact, be a couple of inches below parallel when seen from the side. Depth misjudgment in the squat may be responsible for your lower back rounding.

While plenty can go wrong in the small exercises, the bigger ones are more complicated. They give greater scope for errors, and much can be learned about the impact of adjustments in technique.

Using an *unloaded* bar, make small adjustments in your technique, one at a time, and tape yourself from a side view. Provide a commentary so that when you view the film you know what each adjustment is as it's made on the recording. Then you can accurately analyze your technique and the impact of changes. Don't try to rely on memory alone for what adjustment was being made at a given moment in the recording.

Make a recording of the evolution of your technique in the major exercises. This will provide you with a permanent reminder of what you used to do, the changes you made, and the correct technique you're now capable of using. Periodic viewing of the tape will keep you on course for maintaining correct technique.

An example of what to do

Here's an example of how you could go about composing a recording of the evolution of your squatting technique. Do this sort of study for all your major exercises.

First, you need a thorough academic grasp of squatting technique from studying this book. Then, without making any adjustments to your squatting technique, record just three reps done in your old style using your usual 12-rep poundage. Have the recording done from the side view. When you examine the recording you may notice:

1. The bar is placed too high on your shoulders.

2. You bend at your hips before you bend at your knees.

3. You go so low that your lower back rounds.

4. Your knees come inward during the ascent. (It may be difficult to detect this from the side view.)

5. You tend to topple forward a little on the ascents.

If you've been squatting in a style anything like this, you're unlikely to have been enjoying the exercise, or aching in the right areas of your body after a workout. And if you've been getting injured, you know at least some of the reasons why.

Make technique changes, and provide commentary of what you're doing as you go along. Finding the best squatting technique for you needs experimentation and practice. Because you'll be illustrating technique errors as well as improvements, be sure that you use only a bare bar, so that you don't hurt yourself.

Start by lowering the bar on your upper back so that it's positioned on the pad of muscle just above your shoulder blades. Your aim is to hold the bar as low as you can without losing stability during the course of a set. Record a few reps using the new bar position. You may need to widen your grip on the bar to accommodate the lowering of the bar. It may feel awkward to begin with, but you'll soon get used to it.

Now record the impact of stance variations, while keeping other variables constant. Do some reps with your heels hip-width apart and feet parallel to each other. Then do some with the same heel spacing but toes flared. Try a flare on each foot of about 25 degrees, and then about 45 degrees. Then try other heel spacings (wider and narrower) and different degrees of toe flare.

Notice how some set-ups cause you to lean forward more than others, and that some make deep squatting harder than others. Settle on the heel placement and toe flare that feel the most comfortable, stable and powerful.

Record a few squats with the weight felt primarily through your toes. Then do a few with the weight felt almost totally through your heels. And then do a few with the weight felt evenly over the balls and heels.

When viewing the recording, notice the difference to your body alignment (during and between reps) that the different stress distribution over your feet makes. While it may appear to be only a slight difference, slight changes can make a great impact on how an exercise impacts on your body. Add up a few "slight differences" and you'll produce a huge variation that can make the difference between destructive technique, and effective technique.

While keeping all other technique considerations constant, compare the relative speed of your hips and shoulders during the first few inches of the ascent. Record some reps with your hips moving quicker than your shoulders. Then record some with your hips and shoulders rising at the same speed. And then record some with your shoulders rising faster than your hips. Notice the differences in the stress on your lower back, and the path of the bar during the ascent.

If you have the bar too high on your shoulders, and if you start the descent by sticking out your butt, you're going to exaggerate the harm from having your hips rising faster than your shoulders when coming out of the bottom position. Demonstrate and record this. But remember to use only a bare bar (or perhaps just a broomstick) when illustrating very bad technique.

Now put a few errors together—for example, bar too high, stress felt through your toes, and feet parallel to each other. Record the impact made on your squatting technique. Remember to provide commentary of what you're doing, for easy reference and explanation when you play the recording.

Record yourself squatting, with correct technique, to different depths. (Remember to have the camcorder operating from the same height as that of your lower back when you're at the bottom of a squat.) Squat in a power rack where you can set the pins at different heights, to determine depth of descent. Be sure you have some identification for each depth. Number or letter each pin hole so that you have reference points. Note in your commentary that you are, for example, "Squatting to pins set in holes number 29."

Squat to a series of different depths, and examine the impact of the depth changes on your lower back. Determine the depth at which your back just starts to round. Then the pin setting a few inches above that point will become your maximum safe squatting depth.

Now to finish the squat "evolution" video tape: After having studied what has already been recorded, and having acted accordingly to try to perfect your technique, load a barbell with half your usual 12-rep squatting poundage. Do a few perfect reps to the right depth for you. Compare your new technique to the old style recorded prior to all your adjustments. If need be, fine-tune with a little wider foot spacing and a bit more toe flare, for example, to discover even better positioning for you.

There are many components of correct squatting technique. Consider them all when working to discover your optimum technique.

When making an "evolution" recording for other exercises, keep in mind that the biggest exercises are the most complex, have the greatest possibilities for errors, and the largest potential for improvements in technique.

Take video analysis seriously and you'll learn a great deal.

Please note that some of the aforementioned are *incorrect* aspects of technique, for illustrative purposes only. Study the section of this book that covers the squat, for the details of correct technique.

How to become flexible

A flexible body is a requirement for the performance of correct exercise technique. If, for example, your hamstrings (rear of your thighs) are tight, that will proscribe correct squatting technique because it will lead to premature rounding of your lower back. A flexible body is also required for youthfulness, regardless of age.

Although flexibility is an important factor behind the ability to perform the major exercises correctly—for instance, the squat, and the deadlift—there are other important factors, including technique, practice, and inherited leverage factors.

Most people lack sufficient flexibility because of inactivity, or limited activity. Bodyweight and leverages also affect flexibility. A fat person, for example, may be inflexible because of the excess fat getting in the way.

While strength-training exercises can help improve flexibility where suppleness may be lacking, specific stretching is needed, too. Stretching is an important part of a complete exercise program.

Stretching elongates muscles, not tendons or ligaments. Tendons and ligaments are almost inelastic. Muscles need to be lengthened only a little to produce significant improvement in a joint's range of motion.

After a few months of regular use of a balanced program of stretches, you may increase your flexibility substantially. Thereafter you'll need to keep stretching in order to maintain your improved flexibility.

Introductory guidelines

Ideally, stretch immediately after you've done some resistance training, or immediately after a stint of aerobic exercise. Then your muscles will be warm, and many of your joints will be lubricated with synovial fluid. This will help to develop flexibility more quickly, reduce discomfort during the stretches, and decrease the chance of injury. When you stretch at another time, warm up first with five or more minutes of low-intensity work on, for example, an exercise bike, treadmill, or ski machine. Alternatively, go for a brisk walk, walk up and down a few flights of stairs, or do some easy calisthenic exercises for a few minutes. Stretch in a warm room, and keep yourself covered.

Sometimes it's necessary to stretch before you train with weights. This would follow the general warm-up work that should open every strength-training workout. If some muscles are tight, especially on one side of your body only, stretch to remove that tightness. If you don't get both sides equally pliable, you may promote asymmetrical exercise technique, which would increase the risk of injury. For example, assume that your right hamstring muscles are tighter than those on your left. When you squat, the less flexible right hamstrings may stop lengthening while the left ones keep lengthening. That would lead to asymmetrical exercise technique.

Especially prior to squatting and deadlifting, check for flexibility imbalances between the two sides of your body, and invest time in additional warming up and stretching to rectify imbalances. If you're equally stiff on both sides of your body, you may not set yourself up for asymmetrical technique, but you should still invest the time to get yourself loosened up to your normal state of flexibility. During the strength-training routines in this book, specific stretching is recommended immediately prior to squatting and deadlifting.

How to stretch

Stretching is dangerous if done incorrectly. If you try to rush your progress, you'll get hurt. Never force a stretch. Work progressively — within a given workout, and from week to week — until you reach the level of flexibility that you'll maintain. Never bounce while stretching. And avoid holding your breath — breathe rhythmically.

Don't move immediately into your usual level of flexibility for a given stretch. Work into that over several progressive stretches, each one taking you a little further than the previous one. You should feel only slight discomfort as you stretch.

Unless a different procedure is described for a specific stretch that follows, do the minimum of three reps of 20 to 45 seconds for each stretch. Be cautious — do more rather than fewer progressive stretches before getting to your current limit stretch.

As you hold each rep of a stretch, you should feel the muscular tension diminish. Depending on the stretch, and the individual, you may need to hold a stretch for up to 45 seconds (and perhaps even longer) before you feel this slackening. The easing of tension is the signal to relax for a few seconds, then move further into the stretch in order to make the muscle(s) feel tight again. If you don't feel the tension diminishing even after a hold of 45 to 60 seconds, let the stretch go for a few seconds, then slowly move into the next rep.

Never force yourself to feel pain, but you must feel tension during each stretch. Never have anyone force you into a stretch. And never be in a hurry.

Some days you'll be less flexible than on others, so don't expect to stretch equally well every session.

Stretching is a pleasure, if done properly. Enjoy it!

Here are essential stretches for preparing your body for the resistance training promoted in this book. Perform the stretches on three non-consecutive days per week.

Some stretches are performed on the floor. Be careful how you get up from lying supine, or you may irritate your lower back. Don't sit up with straight knees. While on your back, bend your knees and, with your knees held above your chest, briskly roll off your back into a sitting position. As an alternative, roll to one side and, using your hands for assistance, push into a sitting position.

1. Calves

Stand near a support such as a door frame, or a wall. Place the balls of your feet on a book, board, or side-by-side weight plates about half an inch or one centimeter thick, and your heels on the floor. Stand upright, with straight knees, and feel the tension in your calves. You may feel more tension in one calf than the other. After the tension has eased, lean forward until you again feel tension in your calves. After the tension has eased, lean forward a little more, until you feel tension once again. Keep your heels on the floor throughout this stretch.

The stretch may also be done one foot at a time, as illustrated.

Develop symmetrical flexibility.

As the weeks go by, you may need to increase the thickness of the board or plates, to produce the required tension in your calves. If you feel tension behind your knees, you're overstretching or rushing the stretch, and you should ease back.

If your calves are tight, you may not need any elevation to begin with. Work onto the elevation after a few weeks, as your calves increase in flexibility.

This stretch is for the calf muscle, not the Achilles tendon. As noted already, tendons are almost inelastic.

2. Groin muscles and thigh adductors

Sit with your torso vertical and back resting against a wall. Bend your knees while keeping your feet on the floor. Put the soles of your feet against each other at a comfortable distance from your hips, and rest their outside edges on the floor. Your legs and thighs should form a rhombus.

Let gravity gently pull your knees toward the floor. You may feel tension more in one thigh than the other. Hold for about a minute, straighten your knees, adopt the stretch again, and gravity will pull on a more supple lower body.

Keep your torso upright, with your back and head against the wall. Don't round your back, lean forward, bounce, or push on your knees. Haste or incorrect technique may produce a groin injury. You shouldn't feel tension in the area in front of your pubic bone, because that can lead to injury. If there is tension at your pubic bone, move your feet outward, and progress at a slower pace.

Develop symmetrical flexibility.

After at least a month, rest your hands on your knees for added resistance, and after no less than a further month, push downward very gently. But don't force your knees downward.

To progress in flexibility, bring your heels gradually closer to your hips. Progress will be slow, however, so be patient. But before you bring your heels closer to your pelvis, you should be able to place your outer legs flat on the floor at your current foot positioning. The trainee demonstrating this stretch should increase her flexibility at the illustrated foot positioning before moving her heels inward.

Breathe continuously as you stretch. Don't hold your breath.

3. Hip flexors (over the front of the pelvis)

Stand next to a stable box or bench no more than a foot or 30 centimeters tall. Bend your left knee and place your left foot flat on the top surface, with the front of your right foot on the floor about 12 inches (30 cms) behind an imaginary line drawn through the heel of your left foot. Keep both feet pointing straight ahead. Gently and slowly move forward by bending more at your left knee, just enough to produce a slight stretch at the front of your right hip. Keep the heel of your right foot flat on the floor, and your right knee straight. Hold the stretch until the tension eases. Repeat on the other side, then return to the first side once more, and so on.

If you feel the stretch more in your calf than the front of hip, you probably have your rear foot too far back.

Develop symmetrical flexibility. Take great care, and progress slowly. This stretch will involve muscles you may never have stretched before, which may currently be tight. Don't arch your back during the stretch, or bend forward at your waist. Your torso must be straight, and upright, for the required effect on your hip flexors.

If your feet are turned outward, that will increase the involvement   of your thigh adductors. Keep both feet pointing straight ahead. If the rear foot is turned inward a little, that may help focus the stretch on the hip flexors even more.

As your suppleness increases, you'll be able to bend more at your raised knee. Once you can comfortably bend your knee until its shin is vertical or slightly beyond vertical, increase the height of the elevation. Do this half an inch or a centimeter at a time—for example, put a weight plate on the box, or under it. Progress can also be made by gradually increasing the distance between the elevation and your rear foot, up to a maximum of about two feet or 60 centimeters.

Assisted stretch for the hip flexors

After at least a couple of months on the aforementioned hip-flexor stretch, add the following stretch:

Lie on a bench with your hips approximately lined up with the edge, and both knees held toward your chest. Lift your head and shoulders off the bench, and put both hands around your left upper shin. Press your lower back onto the bench, and move your right leg and thigh forward so that they hang loosely off the bench, with your right knee bent only slightly. Let gravity pull on the limb until you feel the tension ease. Repeat for the other side. Perform three stretches for each side. Keep your lower back pressed onto the bench at all times. If your lower back comes off the bench, you risk injuring your back.

You may need to elevate the bench as your flexibility increases, so that you have a greater range of motion.

Develop symmetrical flexibility.

After two months of letting gravity alone pull on your hip flexors, get the help of an assistant. On an elevated bench—to make it easier for the assistant, and to provide sufficient range of motion for you—get in the same position as for the unassisted version. The assistant should hold your ankle with one hand, and your lower thigh with the other hand, and your knee should be only slightly bent. The assistant should apply just sufficient, steady pressure to your thigh so that you feel tension in your hip flexors. Wait until the tension eases, then work the other side. Perform three stretches for each side.

Your assistant must be immediately responsive to your feedback. *Never force the stretch.* And keep your lower back pressed onto the bench at all times.

4. Hamstrings (rear thigh)

Lie on your back with both feet flat on the floor, and knees bent. Straighten your left knee, and lift that limb as far from the floor as is comfortable. Keep your right foot flat on the floor, and your right knee bent—this helps to reduce rotation of your pelvis. And keep your lower back pressed against the floor. Hold your left limb at the

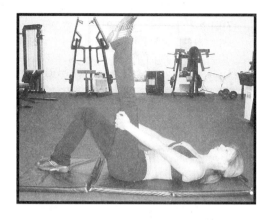

rear of your thigh, or knee, with both hands, and pull gently. Hold this position until the tension in your hamstrings eases, then relax, and repeat. This time you should be able to pull a little further, but still keep your knee straight. Hold this position until, again, the tension eases, then relax, and repeat once more. Stretch your right hamstrings in the same manner.

There should be no tension behind your knee—there's no hamstring muscle behind the knee. If there is tension behind your knee, reduce the tension until it's felt in your hamstrings.

To progress in flexibility, incrementally bring your leg nearer to your face. To help with this, gradually move your hands toward your feet.

For another form of control, use a towel, strap, or belt, and loop it stirrup-like over the arch of your foot, and gently pull on it. Keep your toes above your heel. Don't pull on the ball of your foot, because that would cause your calf to tighten, and mar the stretch for the hamstrings. The calf muscle should be relaxed.

The knee nearest the floor should be bent, not straight as shown here, to reduce rotation of the pelvis. Note how the lower back and the hip bones are pressed against the floor, to prevent the lower back rounding and creating just an illusion of hamstring flexibility.

If this stretch is too difficult, start with the wall stretch. Lie on the floor with your heels against a wall, and knees bent a little. Position yourself close enough to the wall so that you feel slight tension in your hamstrings. Hold this position until the tension eases, then relax, and repeat. This time, straighten your knees to increase tension. To further increase tension, move your hips closer to the wall.

Develop symmetrical flexibility.

Symmetrical flexibility

You may find that muscles of one limb, or on one side of your torso, are less flexible than those of the opposite side. If so, perform additional reps of each relevant stretch on the less flexible side in a one-sided stretch such as Stretch 3; or place greater emphasis on the less flexible side in a two-sided stretch such as Stretch 2. Be patient, and persistent. Over time this should yield symmetrical left-right flexibility unless there are physical restrictions that require treatment—see the box on the next page.

Kneeling—caution

Avoid compression on your kneecap during any activity. Kneecap compression can produce tendinitis, and damage to the underside of the kneecap and the articular cartilage of the thigh bone. This can lead to chondromalacia. When kneeling, don't apply pressure to the kneecap. Keep the pressure on the top part of the shinbone just beneath the kneecap, and even then, minimize the time spent in that position.

5. Buttocks

Lie on your back with your left knee bent. Put your hands over your shinbone just beneath your knee cap, or over your hamstrings just behind your knee if that's more comfortable. Pull your knee toward your chest until you feel slight tension in your left buttock. Hold that position until the tension eases. Next, without leaning to one side, pull your bent, left knee toward your right side until, again, you feel tension in your left buttock. Hold until the tension eases. Repeat on the other side, before returning to the first side. Press your lower back firmly against the floor at all times. Perform three stretches for each side. Develop symmetrical flexibility.

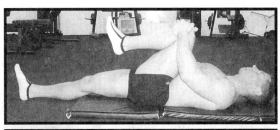
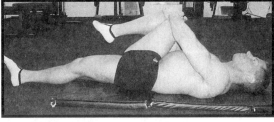

Especially to begin with—and this is not illustrated—you may prefer to keep your resting knee slightly bent.

Difficulty stretching?

If you have difficulties with these stretches, and don't progress in flexibility as the weeks go by, or don't progress symmetrically, you may have scar tissue, adhesions, or other restrictions in your muscles. These need to be treated so that your muscles can return to their normal, supple, efficient, discomfort-free operation.

As an illustration, I struggled with the quadriceps stretch—Stretch 7—for several years, and was never able to progress at it. Then following non-invasive, soft-tissue work (Active Release Techniques®) to remove the restrictions in my thighs—including the removal of adhesions between my right vastus lateralis and right iliotibial band (thigh tissues)—the flexibility in my quadriceps increased instantly. Only then did the quadriceps stretch become effective. A few weeks after treatment I was able to sit on my ankles, which I hadn't been able to for many years.

6. Spine extension

Lie prone with your arms and forearms outstretched. Pull your arms back so that your hands are alongside your head. Raise your head and shoulders sufficiently so that you can rest your forearms on the floor with your elbow joints roughly at right angles. Hold for about 20 seconds, then return to the floor. Relax for a few seconds, then repeat and hold a little longer.

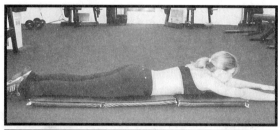

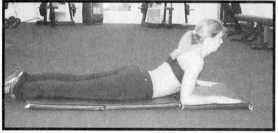

Next, while still on your front, put your hands alongside your chest, or shoulders, depending on your flexibility. Then slowly push yourself up so that your back arches and your elbows straighten. Don't force it. Relax your lower body so that it sags. Hold for only a few seconds to begin with, then return your torso to

The above photograph shows an extended neck AND an extended back. For most people, a NEUTRAL neck is the safest position during this stretch—neither flexed nor extended.

the floor. Do several reps. Over a few sessions, build up the duration of how long you hold the sag, the degree of sag, and the number of reps. *Work into this carefully and progressively.*

Spine extension can be great therapy for back discomfort. It can also help to prevent back pain. Doing this stretch daily can help maintain the natural curves of your spine, which tend to flatten with age.

7. Quadriceps (front thigh)

Stand with your right hand braced on a fixed object. Bend your left knee and lift your left foot behind you. With your left hand, grab your left ankle or leg, not your foot. If you hold your foot you'll load the tendons of your toes, and mar the stretch for your quadriceps. Keep your torso vertical.

Pull on your ankle until you feel tension in your quadriceps. And push your hips forward a little during the stretch. Hold the stretch until the tension eases, then relax. Repeat on the other side, and so on.

Develop symmetrical flexibility.

If you hold your left ankle with your right hand, the stretch is applied differently. The femur would be rotated, which would take the quadriceps out of their ideal functional alignment.

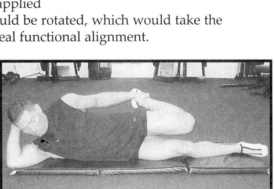

The quadriceps stretch can be done lying. Lie on your right side, with your legs, thighs, and torso in a straight line. Grab your left ankle with your left hand, and follow the same guidelines as for the standing version.

8. Shoulders and chest

Stand upright with your toes about three inches or eight centimeters from the center of a doorway. Place your hands flat against the wall or wooden frame around the doorway. Your palms should face forward, and your arms should be parallel with the floor. The elbow joint is maintained at an angle determined by the width of the doorway and the length of your arms. This is about a right angle for a typical doorway and an average-size adult. Gently and slowly lean forward, and feel the stretch in your shoulders and pectorals. Don't overstretch. Don't force your shoulders forward. As your torso leans forward, your shoulders will move forward, too. Keep your heels on the floor, and don't allow your body to sag.

To progress in flexibility as the weeks go by, step back a little from the doorway, but maintain your hand placement. Then there'll be more tension in your shoulders when you lean forward.

Stretch #9, additional tips

For stability during this obliques and spinal musculature stretch, distribute the stress over your feet in a 50-50 split. And while you bend to the side you should take more of the stress on the inner sides of your feet than the outer.

9. Obliques (sides of your torso), and spinal musculature

Stand with your feet together, or almost together, and knees straight. With your hands resting on your hips, push your hips to your left and simultaneously lean your torso to your right. Lean to the point where you feel slight tension in your left side. Hold until the tension eases, then return to the upright position. On the return, lead with your *torso* and let your hips follow—don't bring your hips back first, because that could cause irritation or injury. Repeat on the other side. Perform three stretches for each side.

All movement should be lateral. Don't lean forward, or backward.

After a few sessions, perform the stretch with your forearms crossed on your chest. The raised hands will increase the resistance. After a few more sessions, or when you're ready, put your hands on your head, to increase resistance further. Later on still, perform the stretch with your arms straight overhead, hands together—reach out with your hands as far as possible while you lean to the side.

A wider stance may provide greater stability, but a less effective stretch. If stability is a problem, use a hip-width stance to start with, then after a few sessions, as you improve your stability, gradually reduce the width of your stance.

This isn't just a stretch. It will also strengthen your obliques, and some of your spinal musculature.

The illustrations show the advanced form of this stretch. See the text for the less demanding versions.

Develop symmetrical flexibility. But take great care—*progress slowly*. This stretch will involve muscles you may never have stretched before, and which may be tight currently.

10. Neck, back, and obliques

Sit sideways on a chair that doesn't have arms, as illustrated. (In a gym, you could use an adjustable bench that can be set at a high incline, to simulate a chair.) Keep your knees bent at about a right angle, and feet flat on the floor about shoulder-width apart. Rotate to your right and grab the back of the chair with both hands. This is the starting position.

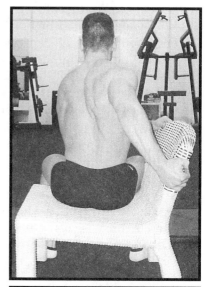

Rotate your torso and neck further to your right. Gently rotate your spine. Stay *upright*—don't slouch—and keep your buttocks and thighs on the seat. Rotate to the point where you feel slight tension in your back, obliques, and neck. Hold until the tension eases, then return to the starting position. Pause for a few seconds, and repeat. Perform three stretches for each side.

Develop symmetrical flexibility.

But take great care—progress slowly. This stretch will involve muscles you may never have stretched before, and which may currently be tight.

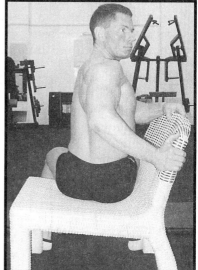

11. General knee flexibility test, and lower-body stretch

A general test of knee flexibility is the ability to sit on your heels while kneeling on the floor with your thighs and feet together. If you can't do this comfortably, you may not, yet, have the required flexibility or knee health to squat safely and effectively. Sit on your heels for 15 to 30 seconds, two or three times, as part of your stretching routine.

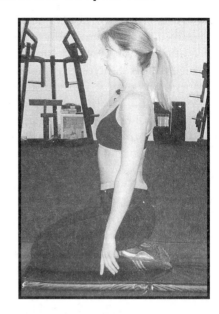

If you can't sit on your heels, perform the stretch with two or more stacked, thick books on the floor between your heels. (Your feet would have to be spaced accordingly.) Sit on the books. As your flexibility increases, incrementally reduce the height of the stack of books. It may require a few weeks of regular stretching, or longer, before you can sit on your heels. Make progress gradually.

A good preparatory exercise for this stretch, is *Stretch 7*.

12. Post-workout spine stretch

After every workout (once you're training in a gym), and especially after deadlifting and squatting, gently stretch your spine, to help keep it healthy. Hang from an overhead bar, or some other support, with a shoulder-width grip, and relax your lower body so that it gently pulls on your spine, to relieve compression from your vertebrae. Bend your knees a little, then raise them a few inches, or about ten centimeters, for a better stretch. Start with ten seconds per hang, and build up over a few weeks to 30 seconds per rep.

If you have shoulder or elbow problems, be careful, because the hanging could aggravate the problems. Don't relax your shoulders. Keep them tight.

Rather than perform this stretch with straight legs, as illustrated, bend your knees a little, then raise them a few inches, for a better stretch.

If you have purpose-built inversion-therapy equipment available (not illustrated), use it as an alternative to the overhead bar. But don't invert yourself for longer than one minute at a time, and work into that progressively over several weeks. Longer periods of inversion may irritate your spine rather than help it.

An alternative to purpose-built inversion-therapy equipment is the use of a back extension apparatus. You can use the 45-degree apparatus, or the traditional set-up.

Use of the traditional back extension apparatus for inversion therapy (left), and the 45-degree set-up (above).

Another possibility is to use bars designed for the parallel bar dip. Get in position with your elbows straight, and your shoulders tight (don't slouch), and then relax your lower body. Done correctly, you'll feel a gentle stretch in your spine. Start with ten seconds per stretch, and build up over a few weeks to 30 seconds per rep

As well as one of these three spine stretches, perform *Stretch 6* after each workout.

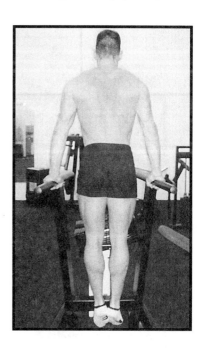

Implementing the stretching routine

This routine, with three reps for each stretch, can be completed in 15 to 30 minutes, depending on how long you hold each rep.

Don't consider the stretching as a burden on your time. It's an investment. When done properly, it's an injury-proofing, health-promoting, and enjoyable supplement to your training program.

Recommended reading

THE STARK REALITY OF STRETCHING (1997, The Stark Reality Corp.), fourth edition, by Dr. Steven D. Stark

---

More on stretching

Stretching increases the length of muscle fibers. The lengthening occurs through individual muscle fibers growing in length within a muscle because of the addition of sarcomeres—tiny contractile units. Additionally, the connective tissue in and around the muscle is expanded, including the fascia that surrounds the bundles of muscle fibers, and the wrappings of individual fibers. Fascia is a band or sheath of connective tissue, and it also supports, binds, covers, and separates muscles and groups of muscles, and organs, too.

Nerves also respond to stretching. Nerves don't take a straight course through the tissues that surround them. When stretched, the nerves are pulled straight somewhat. Beyond that lengthening, the meandering path of the individual fibers *within* a nerve can also be straightened in response to a stretch. Furthermore, the enveloping connective tissue has sufficient elasticity to accommodate some additional stretch without damaging the enclosed nerve fibers.

Strength training that uses full ranges of motion can help to promote flexibility, but there are some motions that strength training doesn't typically cover. Furthermore, some strength-training exercises can't be performed over the fullest possible ranges of motion because, under the load of progressive resistance, those exercises are dangerous for most trainees. A good stretching routine can, however, cover those ranges of motion safely.

A supple body isn't valuable merely to help enable correct performance of strength-training exercises. Without a supple body, movements in general become restricted, there's reduced resilience or give in the body to withstand sudden movements safely, dynamic balance is impaired, and the loose connective tissue of the body loses its lubricating properties. (Loose connective tissue fills the spaces between muscle, nervous, and epithelial tissue, and between bone and cartilage, tendons and ligaments, and joints and joint capsules.) Therefore, without a supple body, muscles lose some of their elasticity and ability to function smoothly, and tendons, ligaments, and joint capsules become brittle. Tissues in general become more susceptible to injury, and the body ages at an accelerated rate.

Should there ever be excessive flexibility, which is extraordinary, ease back on stretching. The muscles will get shorter, and the connective tissues will soon follow suit.

Hatha yoga

After a few weeks of following this stretching routine, consider expanding it. Then, hatha yoga postures are recommended. But if done incorrectly, these postures will produce injury. Employ warm-ups followed by a sequence of main postures intermingled with rest postures and compensation (or counter) postures, selected by an expert teacher. And make progress *slowly*.

Hatha yoga is one of the eight branches of yoga—the best known branch in the West. Hatha yoga is an ancient system of exercise that's revered by millions of people. The practice of hatha yoga develops flexibility, and promotes many other health benefits. Physical postures comprise the main part of hatha yoga.

Hatha yoga doesn't require freak-show flexibility, and doesn't have to have anything to do with chanting, gurus, or religion. You don't need to learn any strange jargon, Sanskrit names, or New Age philosophy. And hatha yoga is for women *and* men. Some top athletes in professional sports have discovered the benefits of hatha yoga.

For an introduction to hatha yoga, and to find out about how some star athletes use it as part of their program for peak performance, see John Capouya's book. See the other book for a deeper introduction to yoga.

REAL MEN DO YOGA (2003, Health Communications), by John Capouya
YOGA FOR DUMMIES (1999, Wiley), by Georg Feuerstein, and Larry Payne

About the author

I was born in 1958 in Stockton-on-Tees, England. I started resistance training at age 14, when I got a set of chest expanders. In 1973 I started weight training, in a gym at a local community center. That became the focus of my life until, in 1978, I went to college in Liverpool, England, where my single-minded dedication to bodybuilding continued. This included working out at a bodybuilding gym where one of Europe's leading physiques trained. We often worked out at the same time.

This man helped me to learn a major lesson. He was on bodybuilding drugs and, generally, was a genetic phenomenon for bodybuilding. But I had better calf development even though I was drug-free and had been training for far fewer years. He even asked me for advice on how he could improve his calves. *The explanation for the difference in our calf development was solely in our heredity.* I had better genetics for calf development, but he was much better off in all other bodyparts. *I trained my calves like I trained my arms, chest, and shoulders, but my calves were much more responsive than those other muscle groups.* And he hadn't neglected his calves. He knew they were his weakness.

Muscles were more important than everything else in my life. I craved to be a professional bodybuilder. School work, social activities, and sport were neglected in my quest to build a great physique.

Despite 100% commitment to bodybuilding, my initial gains were only modest. After getting even more "serious" about my training—increasing its volume, frequency, and intensity—progress came to a halt. Then started my appreciation of "hard gaining."

I learned that there was much more to account for bodybuilding success than effort and dedication. As well as the critical role of heredity, I also learned about the need to use training routines appropriate to the individual, and not to imitate the training methods used by people who have great genetic advantages for bodybuilding. Then, instead of further years of stagnation and frustration, I had years of training progress, and satisfaction.

I was motivated to share these lessons with others. I wrote my first article while at college, and had it published by Peary Rader in the June-July 1981 issue of IRON MAN, an American magazine. In addition to writing many further articles for IRON MAN, I started writing for a number of US- and UK-published bodybuilding magazines.

I graduated in 1982 but was unable to find a teaching post in England. I sought employment overseas, and in January 1983 I started teaching at an international school on the Mediterranean island of Cyprus.

In 1989 I founded CS Publishing, and started my own magazine called THE HARDGAINER (later changed to HARDGAINER). During 1991 I finished writing BRAWN. In 1993 I gave up school teaching and worked solely for CS Publishing. Over the next seven years I wrote THE INSIDER'S TELL-ALL HANDBOOK ON WEIGHT-TRAINING TECHNIQUE (the first edition), THE MUSCLE AND MIGHT TRAINING TRACKER, BEYOND BRAWN, and FURTHER BRAWN.

In 2001 I started BUILD MUSCLE, LOSE FAT, LOOK GREAT, and completed it in late 2005. In early 2004 I retired HARDGAINER. Then I had the time required to maintain book production yet broaden my interests and activities beyond training, including becoming a provider of Active Release Techniques®.

And since starting in 1981 I've continued to write articles on a regular basis for international training magazines.

I had wanted to be a professional bodybuilder, but it was an unattainable goal because my heredity didn't provide me with the potential to build huge muscles. Furthermore, I was unwilling to take bodybuilding drugs. But the lessons I learned did, nevertheless, enable me to transform my body.

I didn't become a professional bodybuilder, but I did make a career out of my passion for training, and physique transformation. And the lessons I learned, many of which are detailed in this book, can enable you to transform your body.

I continue to live in Cyprus with my wife and our two daughters.

Stuart's other publications

I. BUILD MUSCLE, LOSE FAT, LOOK GREAT

2. HARDGAINER magazine

3. BRAWN

4. BEYOND BRAWN

5. THE MUSCLE AND MIGHT TRAINING TRACKER

Each of these has unique value to complement what THE INSIDER'S TELL-ALL HANDBOOK ON WEIGHT-TRAINING TECHNIQUE teaches. Once you've studied INSIDER'S, you may want to read some of the other publications, for additional instruction and information.

BUILD MUSCLE, LOSE FAT, LOOK GREAT

First published in 2006, this is Stuart's most complete book. At 640 pages, and with nearly 400 photographs, it has an extraordinary quality and quantity of instruction and information.

It's the definitive guide for men and women of all ages. And it's for you if you're a beginner or even if you have many years of training experience.

About 200 pages are devoted to exercise technique, to provide the most complete descriptions on the market outside of **THE INSIDER'S TELL-ALL HANDBOOK ON WEIGHT-TRAINING TECHNIQUE**. But that still leaves about 400 pages to cover everything else related to training.

"Stuart's authoritative book is crammed with responsible, safe, and highly effective instruction. It has my unreserved, professional endorsement."
– *Dr. Gregory Steiner, DC*
Dallas Integrated Health Care, Texas, USA

"A brilliant book! Follow The Program developed by Stuart and you'll reach your potential for strength, muscle mass, fitness, and health."
– *Richard Winett, Ph.D.*
A professor at Virginia Tech, publisher of MASTER TRAINER, and award-winning health researcher

"Utterly complete, a book for men and women who want to 'be in shape,' or to compete at the highest level. All the required information is here."
– *Kathy Leistner, BA, MA, MS, exercise physiologist, past competitor at national and world powerlifting championships, and a former Ms. California*

BUILD MUSCLE, LOSE FAT, LOOK GREAT costs $34.95 (or £22.95 in the UK).

HARDGAINER magazine

From July 1989 until its retirement in early 2004, there were 89 issues of HARDGAINER. It provided more result-producing advice for bodybuilders and strength trainees than was available in any other magazine. It was free of mainstream hokum, but crammed with practical advice, and wisdom.

It spoke to the typical individual. But average potential doesn't have to mean average achievements. In fact, an impressive physique and a terrific level of strength are well within your reach. They key, though, is in the right approach. That's what HARDGAINER was about. Fresh information, and the expertise and experiences of a range of contributors can be found in each issue. And there's plenty of grassroots material, to show you the ins and outs of the practical reality of training.

The content of HARDGAINER doesn't date. The back issues represent a wealth of experience and advice. HARDGAINER includes such features as:

- Inspirational pieces on developing the right training philosophy for you.

- Sample workouts for bodybuilders, powerlifters, and strength trainees.

- Advice for new, intermediate, and advanced trainees.

- Guidance on the psychology of training.

- Exercise equipment; and training in home gyms, and commercial gyms.

- "From the Grassroots" articles, success stories, and readers' letters.

- Questions and answers on all aspects of training and related topics.

- Guidance and tips on nutrition, and recuperation in general.

- Biographies, and interviews.

- Guidance on the treatment and prevention of injuries.

And Stuart edited each issue, and contributed to every one, too.

While most of the first 44 issues are in photocopy format, all the others are in original format although some of them will be in that format for a limited period only. All the back issues are available, however. The contents of each issue are listed at www.hardgainer.com.

Each magazine originally cost US $5.50 (or £3.50, in the UK), inclusive of postage and handling. Order six or more copies at a time, directly from Cyprus, and get them for just US $3.00 each (or £1.75, in the UK).

Specially reduced prices for HARDGAINER.

BRAWN

BRAWN is the classic book that started a training revolution, first published in 1991. BRAWN focuses on genetic realities, appropriate role models, and most of the ins and outs of successful drug-free training. It's especially strong in the philosophical underpinning behind rational training. It also details how the genetically blessed are gifted, and shows why conventional training is so unproductive for typical people.

BRAWN *is now in a 230-page, third edition, from 2007.*

"BRAWN *bowled me over. It's an exceptional nuts and bolts compilation of productive training practices; so exceptional, in fact, that it's avant-garde.*"
– Jan Dellinger
York Barbell Company

"*Are you tired of all the look-alike bodybuilding books? Are you tired of buying little more than a collection of photos of bodybuilding superstars and a pile of routines that will never work for the average person? Here's something different.*

"*If you thought Arnold Schwarzenegger put Graz, Austria on the bodybuilding map, how about Stuart McRobert and Nicosia, Cyprus? Imagine, one man, on a Mediterranean island, who has the audacity to directly challenge most contemporary bodybuilding advice. Instead of being yet another me-too bodybuilding book, McRobert's* BRAWN *is unique: Its tone is serious, its manner evangelical, but most important, its focus is on things that actually work for the average trainee. 'Drugs are evil and the scourge of bodybuilding,' says McRobert, in effect, 'and forget about Mr. O-type training—it just won't work for most people. I'll tell you about some things that do work.'*

"BRAWN *has most bodybuilding books beaten hands down in the depth department, but its biggest contribution just might be its breadth:* BRAWN *introduces you to 90-some percent of the factors that will determine your ultimate success in the gym. This is a very useful book, which can help a lot of people make tremendous bodybuilding progress.*"
– Randall J. Strossen, Ph.D.
Publisher of MILO

"BRAWN *has no hype, no bull, and no commercial messages. It's the real thing and genuinely needed in this field.*"
– Dr. Ken E. Leistner
Co-founder of Iron Island Gym, New York

BRAWN *costs $19.95 (or £13.95, in the UK), plus $5.00 (or £3.00) for postage and handling.*

BEYOND BRAWN

BEYOND BRAWN is 512 pages of information about every facet of bodybuilding, and weight training in general. ***Now in a second edition, from 2006***.

This book is not just for novices. It can save you years of wasted toil regardless of your level of training experience. It will propel you into the detailed, practical know-how needed to turn you into an expertly informed bodybuilder or strength trainee. You can learn all of this from just a few weeks of serious study. Then apply what you learn and you'll develop a degree of muscle and might that will make a mockery of what you would have achieved had you stayed with other training methods.

BEYOND BRAWN will take you right "inside" weight training, to study the practical reality of applying knowledge. It's not a theoretical treatise, or a pack of pseudo-scientific hokum.

> "For bodybuilding instruction, BEYOND BRAWN is par excellence, featuring an unprecedented depth of practical, relevant and readily applicable training information. Even more than that, the book is a training partner, companion, friend, and labor of love. A truly exceptional book!"
> – Jan Dellinger
> *York Barbell Company*

> "BEYOND BRAWN is the most comprehensive, helpful and honest book on natural strength training today. With great care and in extraordinary detail this book covers every training-related topic you can imagine, and without any hype."
> – Bob Whelan, MS, MS, CSCS.
> *President, Whelan Strength Training*

> "BEYOND BRAWN is the bible of rational strength training . . . Page after page is jam-packed with practical, real-world training information that you just cannot find anywhere else . . . This book has my highest endorsement—it's without a doubt the very best book on strength training I've ever read."
> – Kevin R. Fontaine, Ph.D.
> *Assistant Professor of Medicine*
> *Johns Hopkins University School of Medicine*

BEYOND BRAWN *costs $29.95 (or £17.95, in the UK).*

THE MUSCLE & MIGHT TRAINING TRACKER

This 136-page workbook contains everything you need to track your progress—day by day, week by week, month by month, year by year.

A training journal is indispensible for keeping you on track for training success. No matter where you are now—180-pound squat or 500, 13-inch arms or 17, 135-pound bench press or 350—the systematic organization and focus upon achieving goals that a training journal enforces, will help you to improve your physique steadily and consistently. While most trainees are aware of the potential value of a training log, few actually keep one; and that's one of the major reasons why they make minimal or no progress.

There are sample filled-out log pages, and then many detailed blank log pages. The log pages track not only the specifics of your weight training—exercises, set-up details, sets and reps, poundages, and a comments area for each workout—but also nutrition, sleep, and body composition.

As simple as it is to use a training log, don't underestimate the critical role it can play in helping you to maximize your training productivity.

One training log will track your progress for at least 24 months—that's a cost of just $1.00 per month. And this log is built for the job it's designed to do. For example, its robust paper provides the strength to withstand heavy use, and the spiral binding enables the book to open flat for ease of use when entering data. This is no ordinary training diary.

THE MUSCLE & MIGHT TRAINING TRACKER costs $19.95 (or £13.95, in the UK).

ORDER FORM

HARDGAINER

☐ Order six or more copies at a time directly from Cyprus for just US $3.00 each (or £1.75, in the UK). Please specify which of the 89 issues you want:

_____

BUILD MUSCLE, LOSE FAT, LOOK GREAT

☐ $34.95 US, or £22.95 UK

BRAWN

☐ $19.95 US, or £13.95 UK

BEYOND BRAWN

☐ $29.95 US, or £17.95 UK

THE MUSCLE & MIGHT TRAINING TRACKER

☐ $19.95 US, or £13.95 UK

For a single book, please add $5.00 or £3.00, for p&h.

Order any two books and there's no charge for p&h.

Name _____

Address _____

_____ State & zip/code _____ Country _____

CS Publishing Ltd., P.O. Box 20390, CY-2151 Nicosia, Cyprus
email: cspubltd@spidernet.com.cy   tel: +357-2233-3069
Please allow 3–5 weeks for delivery upon receipt of order in Cyprus.

In the US, please pay by check or money order. Checks need to clear. No US or Canadian Postal Money Orders. In the UK, please pay by cheque or postal order.

Money-back guarantee

If you're not fully satisfied with our publications, return within 60 days what you bought and you'll receive a full refund.

Online ordering at www.hardgainer.com

Table of contents

Introduction   10

PART 1

How to train safely   14
Rep speed and control   28
The four main hand grips   30
A primer on anatomy   32

PART 2
How to master exercise technique   46

1. Back extension   basic back extension   54
                           45-degree back extension   57
                           spinal extension   57
                           machine back extension   58

2. Bench press   barbell bench press   60
                           dumbbell bench press   68
                           close-grip bench press   72
                           incline barbell bench press   76
                           incline dumbbell bench press   80

3. Calf raise   standing two-legged calf raise   84
                           standing one-legged calf raise   86

4. Chin-up (and pull-up)   88

5. Crunch   basic crunch   94
                           modified basic crunch   96
                           machine crunch   97
                           reverse crunch   98
                           twisting crunch   100

6. Curl   seated dumbbell curl   104
                           incline dumbbell curl   105
                           barbell curl   106
                           hammer curl   107

7. Deadlift   deadlift (basic, or conventional deadlift)   112
                           parallel-grip deadlift   122
                           partial deadlift   130
                           sumo deadlift   134

8. Finger extension   136

9. Hand-gripper work   torsion-spring gripper   139
                           Ivanko super gripper   141

10. Lateral raise   dumbbell lateral raise   144
                           machine lateral raise   145

11. Leg curl   146

12. Leg press		150
13. L-fly		156
14. Neck work	manual resistance neck work	161
	four-way neck machine	162
15. Parallel bar dip		164
16. Press	seated barbell press	168
	seated dumbbell press	172
17. Pulldown		176
18. Pullover	machine pullover	180
	breathing pullover	184
19. Pushdown		186
20. Rotary torso		188
21. Row	one-arm dumbbell row	190
	cable row	192
	seated machine row	196
	prone low-incline dumbbell row	197
22. Shrug		198
23. Side bend	dumbbell side bend	203
	pulley side bend	205
24. Squat	squat (conventional or back squat)	212
	front squat	230
	ball squat	240
	hip-belt squat	244
25. Timed hold		250

Supplementary exercises

26. Grip machine training	254
27. Lever bar work	256
28. Overhead lockout	258
29. Pinch-grip lifting	262
30. Rader chest pull	266
31. Wrist roller training	268

PART 3

How to handle weights between exercises	274
How to compose exercise technique checklists	280
Video recordings: the acid test of correct exercise technique	282
How to become flexible	288
About the author	308